The CLAAS combine story

Manfred Baedeker · Ralf Lenge

The **CLAAS** combine Story

A family company changes the shape of farming

Landwirtschafts**verlag** GmbH
Münster-Hiltrup

Landwirtschaftsverlag GmbH, 48084 Münster, Germany

© Landwirtschaftsverlag GmbH, Münster-Hiltrup, 2002

Printed in Germany

ISBN 3-7843-3160-2

PREFACE

Without a doubt, no other company has contributed as much to the development of the combine harvester as Claas.

The story of the Claas combines goes hand in hand with the conquest of mechanised harvesting in Europe. For the first time this book provides the whole background on how the combine harvester and with it the German-based company developed.

We wish to thank Claas, who generously made their company archives available. Plenty of data and information along with a large number of pictures were put at our disposal. We would also like to thank the wide range of Claas people with whom we talked and who helped us with their suggestions, including former staff members who had lived through the combine story and had their own special role in the things that happened. Amongst others we would like to mention Dr Ludwig Caspers and Manfred Wagner who both supported us with putting the text together. In addition we received outside support, in particular from Dr Dieter Barth who researched and authored some of the chapters.

Manfred Baedeker / Ralf Lenge

LIST OF CONTENTS

5 | Preface

8 | the combine harvester comes of age

20 | The Claas family

26 | The first German combine — still with teething problems

30 | The breakthrough at Zschernitz

38 | A small and successful "test department"

42 | A Super idea

50 | The godfather of the combine harvester in Germany

52 | The first self-propelled Claas combine

56 | Combine harvester and implement carrier in one

59 | The Columbus conquers the harvest

62 | Combine harvesters boom in the sixties

64 | The entry of even bigger combines

67 | Gigantic — 35 years in service

69 | Suddenly appearances count

72 | Cosmos, Consul and Co.

76 | From pressed steel seats to the cockpit

82   **Compact combines for small farms**

84   **The Claas Jumbo**

85   **Endurance testing in rice**

88   **The Tiger in the rice paddy**

90   **Another new dimension**

97   **Up hill and down dale**

101   **Eight cylinder power pack**

106   **A messy business**

108   **A third drum takes the strain off the straw walkers**

111   **A clean cut is vital**

118   **Threshing close to the Arctic Circle**

120   **Two rotors instead of straw walkers**

124   **The story is far from over**

126   **Claas company chronology**

138   **Model list**

142   **Model index**

THE COMBINE HARVESTER COMES OF AGE

The combine harvester made its first appearance in 1830 in North America and Australia. The first machines that could be used in European conditions took another 100 years to materialise.

There are thousands of inventions in farming which contributed to reducing manual labour. Without a doubt, the combine harvester revolutionised farming more than any other invention. Back in 1800 it took farmers over 100 man hours to harvest a ton of grain. The discovery of the steam or electrically driven threshing machine cut this to half an hour. Today's combines carry out the complete harvest in one go and require no more than 0.03 man hours per ton harvested.

The advantages of combine harvesting were first appreciated by farmers in America and Australia because the vast

Whilst the first combines were being used in America, the European grain harvest was characterised by extensive manual labour.

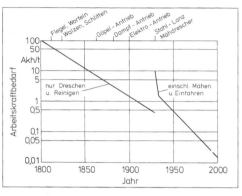

Combining reduced labour considerably. In 1800 over 100 man hours were needed per ton harvested. The combine takes just 0.03 man hours.

areas could hardly be harvested by hand economically. It is surprising that the developments after 1830 took place simultaneously and totally separately at different places on these two continents. The cradles of combine development in America are California and Michigan. Elsewhere in America, the combine was virtually unknown.

The first combine harvester of practical value had a 15 foot (4.50 metre) header. The machine reportedly threshed 600 acres (250 ha) in California. This development was positively influenced by several factors: extensive cultivation methods, the arid climate and farmers who were intrigued by mechanisation. The first combines were home made models created by the farmers themselves. The machines were either trailed or pushed and reached amazing proportions with cutting widths of up to 35 feet and weights as high as 15 tons.

The "power train" consisted of up to 40 horses or mules. It is reported that the first self-propelled combine appeared around 1871 with steam power.

The Americans began to manufacture combines industrially as early as 1860. The machines were built with automatic slope compensation for working across hillsides. By 1889 some 500 combines were running in California and at the end of the 19th century over two thirds of the wheat harvest there was being combined.

Things were different in Europe and it was around this time that the reaper-binder started to spread. Whilst the combination of reaping and binding reduced labour considerably, it was still necessary to stack up the sheaves and transport them. Threshing by means of the stationary threshing machine was an added step that took place in winter.

The first American combines were pulled or pushed by up to 40 horses or mules.

Later, the farmers started using self-propelled steam- or engine-driven machines.

Professor Dr Karl Vormfelde, who was Director of the Agricultural Engineering Institute at the Agricultural College in Bonn during this period was an out-spoken critic of the time wasted in the harvest. He had seen how farmers in America could produce wheat at a low cost and warned of increased competition on the German market.

The first combines made their way from America to Germany in 1928, and by 1930 there were 19 of these machines running in Germany. By way of comparison: there were close to 74 000 combines in operation in America at that time.

These imported combines did not produce impressive results, because the climatic conditions and farm requirements were completely different to

those in America. The harvest period was shorter and the weather was nowhere near as dry and warm. That meant the grain could not be stored directly and needed to be dried first. The straw was damp and used for animal feed and in the stables. This meant that the straw could not be cut as high. In addi-tion, field sizes in Germany and the

Trailed combines were
the most commonly seen
version on American fields.
They worked with cutting
widths of up to 6 metres.

rest of Europe were small and often
surrounded by hedges and this meant
that the big machines could not be
used on them.

Tests were also carried out with these
American combines in Russia and the
results were equally disappointing.
Whilst the German response was to
start thinking about new combine
designs, the Russians tried converting
their combines to run properly in the
prevailing conditions. The threshing
drums and straw walkers were widened
and more space was made available
above the straw walkers. Later, the tine
threshing drum was replaced with one
fitted with threshing bars. This conver-
sion made the "Holt 34" into a Soviet
"Kommunar" with a 4.5 metre cutting
width and the "Holt 36" was christened
the "Stalinetz" with 6 metres cutting
width.

At the same time the Australians came
up with the stripper header. This type
of combine harvester combed the ears
of grain and pulled them off the stem.
This approach was also unsuitable for

the conditions in the Central European
area, although it did become a serious
contender in other markets versus the
US rivals. To underscore this point: over
10 000 stripper combines were shipped
to Argentina between 1902 and 1944.

Meanwhile, hopes faded in Germany
that combining would catch on in the
centre of Europe. Demand was dealt
a further blow by the high unemploy-
ment at that time, because this put
labour-saving devices way down on the
list of priorities. Once again, Professor
Vormfelde pointed out the need for a
European combine in an article entitled
"A new world order with the combine
harvester" published on the 7th of
February 1931 in the journal of the VDI
or German Engineers' Association.

Overseas combines
simply did not fit on the
small-scale European farm
structures, due to their
gigantic proportions.

The MDB from Claas was the first combine harvester that worked properly in German conditions.

Their were two approaches to the new combine development, which took place side by side. A company in Berlin (die Deutschen Industriewerke) built a combine in 1931. In this design the normal reaper was linked up to a stationary thresher. The threshing drum and sieves were fitted in between the feed intake of the reaper and the straw binder. The two machines could be separated again and used individually.

There were several paddles fitted around the drum to generate an air flow to separate the grain from the straw. This mixture of grain and straw passed to a sieve conveyor behind the drum. The conveyor ran over eccentrically mounted discs to produce a shaking motion. From here, the grain went to a grain tank and the chaff into a box. Even though this idea looked promising and was sponsored by the Ministry of Food, the company later gave up their development efforts.

August Claas also began in 1930 to develop a combine with the support of Professor Vormfelde. He persisted in the face of many setbacks and brought the first useable combine onto the market in 1937. From here on, 1 400 units were built in the five years up to 1942. Another eight manufacturers saw a good opportunity here and began developing and building combines after the war.

Claas initially experimented with a front mounted header combine design.

There was still a long way to go before the real breakthrough came. After the Second World War, discussion focussed on the binder and threshing machine, as well as threshing crops from the swath. It was soon realised that the combine harvester could enable the whole grain harvesting process to be mechanised. Even small farmers with just a few acres would benefit. Grain losses could fall to a level of 3 to 5%, a level which had been inconceivable up till then.

The yield would also go up by 5 to 10%, because the grain could ripen better on the stalk.

The combine got a further boost from new varieties with better standing properties, less grain fallout and more consistent ripening plus an improvement in the grain to straw ratio.

The pull type combine dominated this first wave of mechanisation. From 1950 onwards the manufacturers began developing in parallel the first generation of self-propelled units. The best-selling combines of that period in Germany were the so-called "farmers' combines" from Lanz (MD 150), IHC (D61) and MF (MF 30). They were sold for around 9 990 DM without the straw baler. Then the American producers started sales in other countries, and were able to sell at very low prices thanks to their economies of scale.

Large farms were the first to experiment with the first combines. They were on the outlook for labour-saving alternatives to the traditional manual harvest process.

The bagging platform with the sack slide and straw baler were standard features on early combines.

In Germany there were twelve combine producers by the time our story reaches the year 1956. Names like Speiser, Unkel, Mengele, Petermann and others came and went quickly. By the early seventies the combine harvester had finally gained full acceptance in Germany. During this period companies such as Bautz, Dechentreiter, Fella or Ködel & Böhm gave up combine production or were taken over.

The combine evolved progressively to one man operation, with the bagging platform being phased out during the sixties and replaced with a grain tank. Then straw harvesting was separated from the grain harvest. It was no hardship to say goodbye to the mounted baler with all the problems of inadequate engine power and baler malfunctions. In addition this separation provided the advantage of better straw drying in a swath.

Engine power increased steadily. From 1960 to 2000 the average power of combine harvesters increased by 4% per year. Threshing drums were even then very wide, in a range from 0.6 to 1.5 metres.

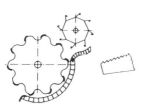

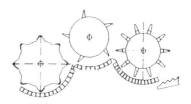

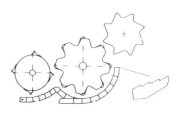

This range of dimensions had been adopted from the stationary threshing machines and in the following years a maximum width of 1.7 metres was reached. This was the limit since any further increase would widen the whole machine beyond the width permissible for road travel in Europe. Increased output could only be achieved by adding to engine power.

The straw walkers also became a limiting factor. They took up a lot of space and there came a point at which there was

not enough room to extend or widen them further. Claas and John Deere improved the aeration and separation with rotary tine systems. In 1974, Ford New Holland came up with a centrifugal separator mounted right behind the threshing drum and designed to reduce the workload on the straw walkers. When the patent on this ran out, other manufacturers developed similar ideas. Deutz Fahr launched the turbo separator in 1987. Former East German MDW followed in 1991 (separator drum), plus Massey Ferguson (rotary separator) and Fiatagri (multicrop scparator).

From 1992, Claas fitted an accelerator drum in front of the threshing drum on most models, aimed at improved grain separation. In the same year, John Deere turned the impeller into a threshing and separation drum. This means that every manufacturer had added a further threshing drum on their high performance models.

An additional drum was fitted either behind or ahead of the main threshing drum to increase the threshing unit's output. This led to a significant improvement in grain separation efficiency.

White and Versatile were hard on their heels and launched similar systems. Two different approaches then became discernible. Some manufacturers retained the right angled threshing drum and replaced the straw walkers with rotary separators. The Claas CS is an example of this approach plus the axial rotors more recently fitted on the Lexion 470 and 480, the New Holland TF combines and the CTS from John Deere.

The companies also busied themselves with alternative threshing and separation systems. This meant finding ways of replacing the classic straw walkers with forced rotor separation. New Holland came on the market first in 1975 in the USA with the TR 70 axial combine. Case International, Allis Chalmers,

The other design approach was to thresh and separate in one step. These axial combines are distinguished by the number, layout and form of the rotors. Case has been selling Axial Flow combines in Europe since 1977. The Gleaner combine from Agco has a right angled

Many manufacturers tried to replace the straw walkers which were a limiting factor to performance. Axial rotors meant a new departure in combine design.

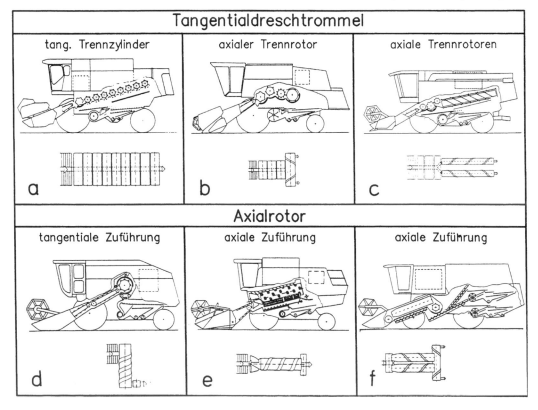

crop flow which makes it too wide for driving on European roads. In 1996, MDW presented the Arcus combine, an axial combine with twin rotors fitted between the front wheels.

Driving and operational comfort gained in importance on combines, because this enabled drivers to extract the most work from the machine during long harvesting days.

As the combine harvester gained in performance, it became increasingly necessary to work on improved driver comfort in order to extract the maximum output from the machine. The first cabs appeared in 1966. The advent of sound insulation meant that the driver lost some contact with the combine as it worked, so control and information systems became more and more important. The spectrum of new gadgets fitted ranged from simple rpm monitors to warning lights and buzzers if something went wrong. Claas launched the first multifunction control lever in 1985. All the important buttons for operating the machine were now grouped together for single-handed operation.

The on-board computer helps the driver set up the combine properly. Control devices monitor each function and the machine's output. Yield mapping helps to improve arable farming inputs and yields.

Hydrostatic transmissions enabled the travel speed to be set precisely and made reversing much easier. Ködel & Böhm were the first to show a combine with this feature in 1965. The system took over despite the higher transmission losses involved.

The advent of on-board computers meant that it became feasible to set up a machine completely automatically. Everything from the drum speed to the sieve box opening could be set based on standard values. Yield mapping was the next major step, enabling yield differences on every individual field to be plotted by linking yield metering to GPS measurement. The yield maps can be used for highly accurate fertilising and spraying procedures.

Automatic guidance of the cutter bar at a predetermined height was a further step to reducing driver effort. In 1976, Claas first presented automatic steering for maize harvesting. The rows of maize were brought into contact with metal sensor rods which sensed the position and sent corrective impulses to the steering control unit.

The enormous number of inventions and a wide range of options has turned the combine into a machine for profes-

sional users. Well-trained drivers are needed to keep the combine running at the limit. These factors determine the return on the high investment required for the brief grain harvest periods.

THE CLAAS FAMILY

The first things that spring to mind when people hear the name of Claas are likely to be combine harvesters, harvesting technology or maybe a traditionally based family company. The following chapter will show your what's really behind the family name, and describes some of the people who have mapped the company's course and contributed significantly to farm equipment development.

It all started with centrifuges

Franz Claas was born on the 17th of March 1859 in Clarholz close to Gütersloh in the northern half of Germany. His father, Heinrich Claas, was a farmer and his mother's name was Katharina. His studies pointed in a veterinary direction, but he soon discovered that he had more of a leaning to technical inventions.

In the beginning Franz Claas Senior developed and produced milk centrifuges. Later he turned his attention to building and repairing farm machinery.

The idea that started it all off was a centrifuge for skimming milk, one that was small enough to make it suitable for farmers. The first model was put together in 1887 and then went into full scale production. The first move towards creating a business was the registration of the "Centrifugenfabrik Franz Claas" (Franz Claas centrifuge factory) in the Royal Prussian company register in 1902.

He employed some 20 to 30 people on his farm. Alongside farming, there were a sawmill, a flour mill, a contracting activity plus a business making and repairing farm equipment.

All four sons — Bernhard, August, Franz and Theo — worked in the parental business, with father Franz as an exemplary teacher. The other members of his family consisted of his wife (maiden name of Prövestmann) and three daughters as well. His second son — August — who was born on December 15th 1887 followed in his father's footsteps: after leaving school with his certificate, he went on a mechanical apprenticeship where he passed his final exams, graduating in 1907 from the Bielefeld craftsman's institute.

Company foundation in 1913

August Claas set up his own company in 1913 with the object of repairing and manufacturing straw binders, with his brothers Bernhard and Franz Junior coming on board a year later as joint owners. However, the three elder brothers were called up for service after the First World War broke out. That meant that the newly founded company came to a standstill for a while. The youngest son, Theo Claas, was meanwhile working on airplane and bridge construction in Brandenburg. He too was then called up in 1916. Father Franz could not keep his own company running during the war without the help of his sons.

The newly founded company came back to life only when all four Claas brothers returned safe and sound from the war, brimming with enthusiasm for their business ventures. In 1919 the Claas brothers purchased an old brickworks in Harsewinkel and set up their business there - this is where the company headquarters have stayed to

1930 was an equally momentous step in the development of the Claas brothers' company. The main success factors of Claas have remained unchanged over the years: the will to succeed, business acumen, persistence and thorough knowledge of farming matters, technical experience and inventiveness.
Claas has always pursued the goals of

The successful company development was built on the cohesion between the Claas brothers (from left): Theo, Franz, August and Bernhard.

this day. Initially the company concentrated on repairing and later manufacturing straw binders. Later fertiliser spreaders were added (1923) and straw balers (1931). The company's future was radically changed with the award of a patent and a successful test by the German farming association (DLG) of their "knotter with upper lip". The knotter symbol became the company's logo and trade mark.

The decision to move into the development of a combine harvester suitable for European harvesting conditions in

improving technology to minimise the drudgery of manual labour whilst improving the cost efficient production of agricultural products.

In addition, there is a special "family cement" (Walter Brenner) that kept the Claas brothers Bernhard, August, Franz and Theo together in everything they did. The company founder, August Claas, confirmed this in 1955 in Brunswick: "The main and enduring basis for our company was the cohesion between the Claas brothers".

They each had their own function in the company based on their leanings and dispositions:

Bernhard Claas
(born 25th May 1885, died 18th February 1955) was primarily responsible for personnel and the factory staff.

August Claas
(born 15th December 1887, died 12th April 1982) was the outstanding business leader with a clear vision of technological matters. He powered the company's fortunes for many years.

Franz Claas
(born 16th September 1890, died 24th December 1965) was known as the "father of tool making" with responsibility for the factory equipment.

Theo Claas
(born 23rd May 1897, died 30th August 1952) was concerned principally with the Claas company's commercial development.

Another person has to be mentioned in this context: Paula Claas (maiden name Siepenkort), who was the wife of August Claas. Paula Claas studied foreign languages and economics and worked alongside her husband during three decades within the company. Together with him and in close consensus with her brothers-in-law, Paula Claas helped build up the company from its modest beginnings. She held

Paula and August Claas built up the business from very modest beginnings.

comprehensive signature rights and spent many years in the export area. She had a close empathy with the social needs of the Claas employees and was described in earlier newspaper articles as the "good spirit of Harsewinkel".

August Claas loved to cycle through the main plant and this gave him the opportunity to have direct contact with the shop floor staff. One story has it that on one of his rounds, he picked up a bolt lying on the floor and asked the worker next to it: "Do you know what that is?". The reply was of course: "It's a bolt, Mr Claas". "No, it's my money", was the response from the company owner with a smile and left the worker scratching his head.

A new generation comes on board

Helmut Claas, who is the eldest son of the company founder, graduated from school to complete a mechanical apprenticeship, followed by mechanical engineering studies at the Hanover

Technical University (1948 to 1954). After this he spent a year in Paris at the Grande Ecole Nationale d'Agriculture before taking on responsibilities in the parental business at an early age. For instance, he planned and implemented the foundation of the sales company in France, which continues to exist today as Claas France SAS.

With his admission to the business in 1958 Helmut Claas devoted himself particularly to engineering and product development. He become a director of the company in 1962.

His father August had determined the company's course from the pioneering days up to the sixties. Following in his father's footsteps, Helmut continued to pursue the goal of running the company as a "family business" and to integrate the members of the family in decision making:

Reinhold Claas
(born 26th March 1931) — second eldest son of August Claas — joined the management in 1957.

Walter Claas
(born 7th September 1931, died 12th March 1979) — the eldest son of Franz Claas — was sales director from 1962 to 1968.

Günther Claas
(born 23rd September 1931) also carried out different management functions, finally in the purchasing area.

1969 — new supervisory board and new management

A new management team was created after a decision taken in the partners' committee at the start of the 1969/70 financial year. A new supervisory board was chosen which consisted of six representatives of the owners and three

After entering the company, Helmut Claas focused on engineering and development activities. August Claas withdrew from management in the sixties.

employee representatives. Dr Manfred Streitbörger, a lawyer, was named as chairman of the supervisory board and Friedhelm Claas was appointed deputy chairman. Reinhold Claas was also nominated as a supervisory board member.

Helmut Claas became a director in 1962. He guided the family company through thirty years of progress.

In 1972 the assets of the earlier legal entity (Gebr. Claas KG) were transferred to the Gebr. Claas Maschinenfabrik GmbH (holding company of the Claas group) and Helmut Claas was elected to the supervisory board. After the company went through a period of economic difficulties, the company structure changed again into Claas OHG on September 1st, 1978 with Helmut Claas as a personally liable partner. Helmut Claas took on the chairmanship of the board whilst August Claas was given the honorary chairmanship.

August Claas passes away aged 94

April 12th, 1982: August Claas, senior director of the company, dies at the age of 94. The whole company says goodbye to its founder, who was honorary citizen and bearer of the ring of honour of the town of Harsewinkel. Over 4 000 guests came to mourn his departure in the main assembly building of the factory. Georg Gallus, the State Secretary of the Federal Agricultural Ministry, characterized the deceased as a great human being, a courageous businessman and imaginative engineer.

During his long life, many honours and awards were granted to the "father of the European combine". These included the federal distinguished service cross, 1st class in 1952, the honorary doctorate

in engineering from the Brunswick Technical University (1955), the distinguished service cross of the order of merit of the Federal Republic of Germany (1957) and the appointment as honorary senator of Hohenheim University (1968).

Helmut Claas, the innovative entrepreneur

In 1995 the Claas OHG legal entity was turned into the Claas KGaA (share owning partnership). Helmut Claas withdrew from the management after three decades of active involvement and took on the chairmanship of the Claas supervisory board and the partners' committee.

Helmut Claas has also received numerous awards and honours: for example, he has been appointed honorary citizen of Harsewinkel in 1986 and received the order of merit of the French agriculture ministry and the medallion of merit of the German state of Baden-Württemberg. Three universities have awarded him the title of a Doctor honoris causa. (Dr. h. c.). The Hungarian Gödöllö University in 1987, Cranfield University in Great Britain in 1998 and the Stuttgart-Hohenheim University in the year 2000.

Claas, a family business

Teamwork has always been a key factor at Claas. There is a strong esprit de corps at all levels and this is the foundation stone for the success of the company. The company management has been fortunate in recruiting, promoting and motivating qualified employees who suit the company's style and have cemented together a uniquely dedicated team. The spirit of the family business is also reflected in a paternal attitude to the employees. Here are just two examples to highlight this approach: a pension fund was created as early as the end of 1975 with the August Claas pension fund. Then the Claas employee participation company (CMG) was founded in 1984. The CMG offers all the employees the possibility of participating in the company's financial success by buying shares in a special company.

The contacts to the retired employees have also been actively pursued at all times by the Claas management to-

gether with the workers' committee. For example there is a "Claas Pensioners' Club" which is supported actively by Claas.

The family partners in the company have taken steps in 2000 to transfer responsibility within the supervisory bodies to the next generation. Helmut Claas's family elected his daughter —

Cathrina Claas — to the partners' committee. Oliver Claas and Volker Claas took the place of their fathers — Günther Claas and Reinhold Claas — on the supervisory board of the KGaA. These steps are designed to ensure the continuity of the family involvement in running the business in future.

A new generation came on board simultaneously with the new millennium. Cathrina Claas, seen here together with Günther and Helmut Claas during the groundbreaking ceremony for the factory remodelling in 2001, now sits on the partners' committee.

THE FIRST GERMAN COMBINE — STILL WITH TEETHING PROBLEMS

Claas wanted to convince both farmers and the agricultural machinery community of the advantages of combine harvesting with the front mounted header.

When he started work in 1930 at Claas in Harsewinkel, the task for Mr Brenner as a designer was clear. The mission was to pursue the development of a combine harvester suitable for European grain conditions including the collection of straw and chaff. What came of the project description was a combine harvester fitted around a 30 hp Lanz Bulldog tractor.

A 2.5 m wide cutter bar was located in front and it could be adjusted to achieve different stubble heights. Special feed chains transported the grain, with the ears hanging downwards, alongside the Bulldog. Behind this a vertical threshing drum was fitted to separate the grain. The drum had a diameter of 35 cm and was 1.2 or 1.0 m high. The stalks were further transported head down, so the remaining grain fell out of the straw. There was no need for straw walkers in this design.

The front mounted cutter bar was wrapped around a Lanz Bulldog tractor. The grain was dispatched alongside the tractor with the ears pointing downwards on a feed conveyor.

The machine laid the straw on the field in a swath. The grain was cleaned with an air flow and sieves and dropped into sacks.

Claas advertised a threshing performance of 40 to 55 hundredweights per hour. Taking contemporary yields into consideration, this corresponded to a work rate of 0.5 to 0.75 hectares per hour. The company built separate rye and wheat combines at that time because of the different stalk lengths. Depending on machine version, wheat could be threshed with a stalk length of up to 1.4 m and rye to 2.0 m.

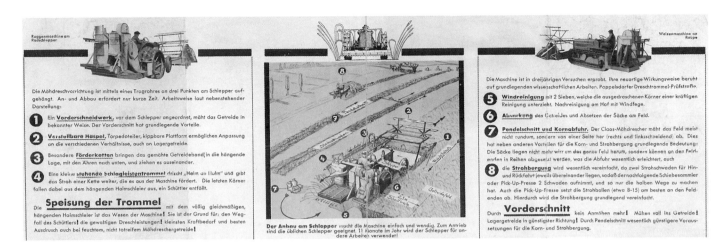

However, Brenner didn't just want to develop a combine with this machine. He also had the complete grain harvest process in mind.

Claas points to the advantages of the combine harvesting method in a little leaflet reproduced above. The company pointed out the decisive advantages over the method predominant till then: considerably lower reaping losses and the reduced weather risk. Mowing, tying and assembling the sheaves were all done away with. The combine took care of all these steps in one single operation. Grain losses could be cut drastically because the machine took the grain on board directly. Brenner calculated an increased yield of one half of a hundredweight of grain per acre. On the basis of 250 acres, this amounted to improved financial proceeds of around 1 250 Marks. By way of comparison, the wheat harvester cost 2 950 Marks and the rye model 3 150 Marks at that time.

Professor Vormfelde of the Agricultural Engineering Institute at Bonn University supported the endeavours of Claas. He wanted to involve the established threshing machine and reaper-binder manufacturers into the development, if at all possible. Therefore a little demonstration was organized close to Bielefeld towards the end of the 1931 harvest. It would appear that the machine did not impress the representatives of the companies such as Fahr, Lanz, Schulze-Standard, Dechentreiter etc. who attended the presentation. After the end of the demonstration, any hope of participation by these companies dissolved into thin air.

The Claas brochure explains the advantages of working with combine harvesters. The sceptics doubted that there would ever be a combine capable of working in difficult European harvests.

August Claas was a farsighted business-man and wouldn't be put off so easily: he coined a decisive phrase to Professor Vormfelde at that time: "If the others don't want to be involved, then we'll make it on our own". Vormfelde made a last attempt in the following year to at least get Lanz back on board for the project with a further demonstration. This demonstration near Zweibrücken also didn't bring about success. From there on, it was definite that the development could only be carried on by

Claas tried out the machine in rice, to check whether it could be used in all crop types. The combine was fitted to a belt drive tractor, so that it could cross the damp fields.

Claas on their own. Another three front mounted headers were built for the next harvest. They worked on the Berlin municipal farms, Malchow farm in Mecklenburg and in the rice harvest in the area surrounding Vercelli in Italy.

The first Claas combine was exhibited at the Imperial Food Production Exhibition in 1934 in Erfurt. However, it was obvious to all concerned that the company had overestimated its capabilities by developing this technology. Brenner said once later: "We developed and made things by hand. Then we built the machines, often on the basis of completely new, unknown feed elements. In the harvest, there were bright spots from time to time when everything went wonderfully. However, after some years of this development, we had to accept that this route was too difficult

and no financial success was likely".
(Source: Farming and its industry. Issel-
stein/Schwarz, published by Verlag Feld
und Wald.)

Another proof of the problems surrounding this innovation is a quotation
from Brenner in the Claas house journal "Der Knoter" on the occasion of his
25th anniversary in the company. He
quotes the remark of a farmer who
had threshed some crops with the test
machine. His answer was a riddle. "It
is a gnom machine". Asked what this
meant, he explained that gnom meant
"Geht Niemals Ohne Monteur". In English: "Never works without mechanic".

Professor Vormfelde and August Claas
made their way to different exhibitions
in Paris, Chicago etc. in the hope of
picking up ideas. Their attention was
attracted to trailed combines, some of
which were equipped with auxiliary
engines. Although the front mounted
header concept of Brenner had some
real advantages, they decided to aban-
don this route and started with the
development of a completely new pull
type combine in 1934.

The subversive "pick-up"

*We would like to provide an
anecdote on a subject that
affected the company in the
period from 1933 to 1945, as
the fanatics in government
went on the hunt for subvers-
ive foreign words. One day,
a letter arrived from the
Ministry of Propaganda, in
which the English term
"pick-up" and its further use
were forbidden.*

*An answer was sent to Berlin,
claiming that this must be a
misunderstanding. "Pick-up" is
an absolutely German word,
in fact a long established term
in Westfalian dialect. In our
part of the world, chickens
"pick" the feed thrown on the
ground "up". This phenom-
enon led us to call our baler
"pick-up", because it does the
same as the chickens, picking
up from the ground to make
dense bales for transport.*

*After some further exchanges
on this matter of national
security, the "Foreign Word
Prevention Headquarters" in
Berlin quietened down and
we were able to continue
using the internationally ac-
cepted term.*

This tongue-in-cheek
account was taken from the
earlier Claas house journal
"Der Knoter" (the knotter).

THE BREAKTHROUGH AT ZSCHERNITZ

Claas succeeded in building the first combine harvester suitable for European harvesting conditions with the MDB or mower/thresher/binder. This combine provided the foundation for all the combines that were to come.

The MDB was the first combine harvester in Europe. The first machine operated on the Zschernitz farm, close to Halle/Saale, to the full satisfaction of the owner. This good result became part and parcel of the Claas history as "the Victory of Zschernitz".

After the difficulties with the front mounted header August Claas had clearly decided in favour of a pull type combine with a transverse crop flow to the threshing drum. However, Professor Vormfelde and engineer Brenner were still supporters of the front mounted header version. They finally fell in line with August Claas's convincing point of view.

The three of them set about designing the new machine, a process that was fraught with difficulties. They tried to

build on the experience with the front mounted header and found that they faced a completely new situation, particularly in the threshing system. The first operational combine and sheaf binder was finally put into the field in 1935.

Once again, this model didn't impress the farmers, though. As it turned out later, 1934 and 1935 were the most critical years for the German combine. At that time, Claas stood alone without any financial support and no potential backers

in sight. During the same period, other economic setbacks had to be coped with. One of the two test combines caught fire by the sparks from a Bulldog and burnt out.

None of this could deter the designers from Harsewinkel and before long they had developed the MDB. The first machine with the serial number 1 was delivered to a farm for the 1936 harvest in a place called Zschernitz, which is in the eastern part of Germany. The machine worked to the complete satisfaction of the owner, Mr Haberland. This fact is remembered as "the Victory of Zschernitz" in the annals of the Claas history.

As of 1937 the MDB was then built in series. By 1939, the hundredth combine had been produced and the thousand mark in the Harsewinkel plant was reached in 1941. As of 1943, Claas was forced to transfer to military production on orders of the government.

The combine making activities were terminated for a while. Altogether 1 400 combines of the MDB type had been produced when the order to stop came through.

The MDB was a pure transverse flow combine. The cutter bar, with 7 feet cutting width, was fitted on the right. It very much looked like the cutter bars used on the reaper-binders of that era.

The grain was fed to the threshing drum on a moving mat similar to the binders. A chain fed the straw around the threshing drum and threw it onto the relatively short straw walkers. The machine was short in length thanks to the large wrap angle of the concave.

The designers went to great lengths to ensure good crop cleaning. The MDB had two stage cleaning as was common on the stationary threshing machines. The first worked with an additional disawner and air suction. The second cleaned with suction and an air blast. The chaff could be blown into a trailed chaff tank on an optional basis. This had two reasons. On the one hand, farmers wanted to keep the chaff and use it as animal forage. On the other hand, they were concerned about weed infestation if the chaff were left on the field.

The grain was filled into sacks on the bagging platform. The straw was dropped onto the field in bundles at the same time. It's worth mentioning that straw binders were the core busi-

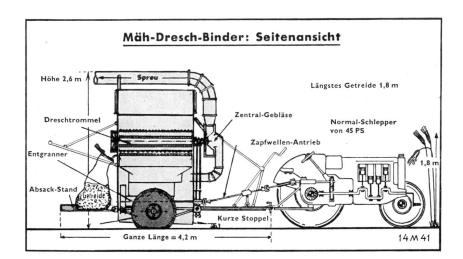

Mäh-Dresch-Binder: Seitenansicht

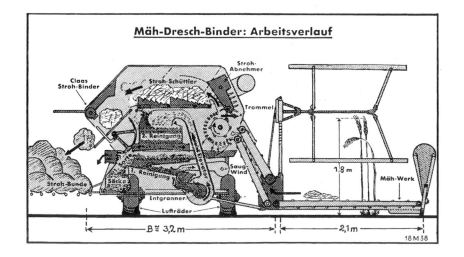

Mäh-Dresch-Binder: Arbeitsverlauf

The crop was transported via a conveyor mat to the threshing drum which was positioned lengthways. The straw was then fed to the binder after crossing the straw walkers and finally ejected to the side. The threshed grains found their way to a chaff sieve with suction and then to the disawner. They then passed through an elevator to the second cleaning stage where they were cleaned again by suction and an air blast.

ness activity of Claas at that time. The company primarily built straw binders and straw balers in Harsewinkel, and these were sold to users of stationary threshing machines.

The cutter bar was removed and hung behind the MDB for road transport. Apart from the chaff collection there were some further additional facilities.

The mechanical slope adjustment enabled angles of up to 15% to be tackled. The sieves needed to be kept as close to the horizontal as possible.

A mechanical slope adjustment for example. There was of course a reason for this too: everyone was used to the fact that stationary threshing machines were always very carefully lined up horizontally and vertically when threshing On the MDB the bagging platform operator could raise the either left or the right wheel with a hand lever. The leaflet explains this feature: "The sieves of the threshing machine must naturally always be kept horizontal, if possible".

There were further options available such as a table that could be fitted for threshing rape. The straw bundles and the full sacks could be gathered optionally. This meant that the bundles and sacks could be put down in crossways rows, to make it easier to clear the field later on.

The MDB was advertised with an output of 1.5 to 2.5 t/h. This figure has to be put into the context of the typical hectare yield of 3 to 5 t. The work rate amounted to 0.4 to 0.7 hectares per hour.

(Left photo)
Claas offered the option of chaff collection. The chaff passed through a flexible metal tube into the trailer. The trailer filled up within an hour or so. During this time, a second trailer could be driven to the farm and emptied.

(Right photo)
The combine throughput was around 25 hundredweight per hour. Claas indicated an annual output of 5 000 hundredweight. Based on yields at that time, this amounted to around 100 ha area.

The large number of functions fascinated cartoonist Ferdinand Barlog who turned the MDB into a combine milling and baking machine.

The MDB weighed 2 400 kg and needed a tractor with 45 hp output for the drive. In addition, a power take off was necessary. The leaflet explains that it takes a tractor driver, a bagging man and a boy to help to operate the combine.

At the time of the Second World War, the export of machines wasn't a very lively business activity. Despite this, there were already one hundred or so Claas combines running in France, Romania, the Netherlands, Denmark and Sweden. Of course everyone was very concerned about patent protection. Therefore the MDB was registered as the only combine with chaff collection in France, Brazil, Hungary, America, Canada, England, Italy and Australia.

The stability and ruggedness of the machine were also excellent and this was confirmed by many praising letters and reports. For example, in 1953 a report appeared in a daily paper in what had become communist East Germany with a picture of an MDB in use. The cartoon-

An article in an East German paper from 1953 on an MDB still working there.

Der **Morgen**

ZENTRALORGAN DER LIBERAL-DEMOKRATISCHEN PARTEI DEUTSCHLANDS

Nr. 175 / 9. Jahrgang   Berlin, Freitag, 31. Juli 1953   15 PFENNIG AUSWÄRTS 20 PFENNIG

Die Volkskammer billigt den neuen Kurs

Zustimmung

Berlin (Eigenber.
der Regierung
Otto Grotew
Innern des
die Volks
34. Volls
am Ab-
erklä-
ger

Ein Griff am Hebel, und schon scheffeln Anneliese und Anita, zwei sächsische Landwirtschaftsschülerinnen, den Roggen ein mit ihrem Claas-Mähdrescher. Während sechs Wochen ihrer Semesterferien helfen sie im Kreis Delitzsch bei der Ernte.

ist Ferdinand Barlog who worked for a Berlin magazine was so taken by the qualities of the MDB that he drew a combine milling and baking machine for his readers.

Claas proceeded cautiously when developing sales during the first years. Nobody was prepared to risk endangering the reputation of the new method by letting it fall into the wrong hands. The idea had not caught on yet, not by a long chalk. The potential customers had to fill out a questionnaire first. This contained questions on the crop sequence, the topography of the farm, the available tractor capacity and the performance expected by the customer. On this basis, it was determined whether the farm was considered suitable for the use of the combine or not.

In addition, great value was placed on training of the staff. At first, mechanics from the factory were sent to set up the combine at the new site. The fitters stayed until the main operator was familiar with the machine. The machine handover was made easier by courses for mechanics and machine operators and these events were planned to take place in Harsewinkel in the quiet winter months.

Good work was rewarded. The factory publicised incentives for good performance with the combine. These competitions were an excellent means to spur the machine crews on to producing higher performance. At the same time, the combine harvester began to receive the recognition it deserved from the farming community.

Prämien für gute Leistungen

Wir schreiben hiermit folgenden **Wettbewerb für die Mäh-Dresch-Binder-Bedienungsmannschaft** aus:

Erreicht eine Maschine im ersten Jahr erstmalig eine Leistung von **200 Doppelzentnern** an einem Tag, so erhält die Bedienungsmannschaft .... **RM. 10,—**

Werden **an 5 Erntetagen je 200 Doppelzentner geleistet** **RM. 20,—**

Erreicht eine Maschine im ersten Erntejahr im Mähdrusch **3000 Doppelzentner,** erhält die Mannschaft .... **RM. 30,—**

4000 Doppelzentner, erhält die Mannschaft .... **RM. 50,—**

Die Zahlenangaben müssen von der Gutsverwaltung gemacht und bestätigt sein. Wir behalten uns vor, diese Angaben zu prüfen. Wir hoffen, daß dieser Wettbewerb ein Ansporn für die Bedienungsmannschaften ist, mit dem M.D.B. recht gute Ernteleistungen herauszuholen.

Gebr. Claas
Abteilung Mähdrescherbau

The factory sponsored competitions aimed at gaining acceptance for harvesting with the combine. The combine team could win up to 50 Marks for producing 4 000 hundredweight, which was a good incentive for them.

A SMALL AND SUCCESSFUL "TEST DEPARTMENT"

Engineer Erich Harmening describes the first modest but very efficient development department at Claas in his own words.

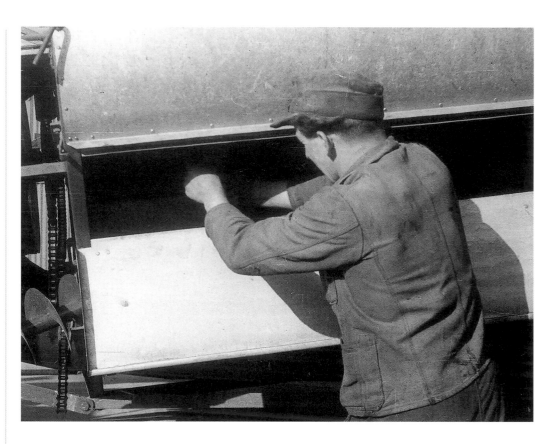

Combine development at Claas took place with the most primitive resources. There were no scientific findings to work upon, so everything had to be done by trial and error.

I must put our "test department", as it was in those days, into inverted commas in view of the present level of the testing technology. For today's designers it is inconceivable how we developed the first combines with simple, really rudimentary resources and managed to put them into series production.

The test department was located in the corner of a factory building in which parts were manufactured for straw balers and binders. The "design office" of Dr Brenner was just 2.50 x 4.00 m in size. A little drawing board stood on one side, and a work bench was on the other side. In addition, the room con-

tained a small desk and some bookshelves. My own drawing board stood outside this room next to a mechanic's vice. The workshop staff consisted of four men.

Dr Brenner had a sectional drawing of a combine on the board on a 1:10 scale, with the most important dimensions and the component arrangements. At first I had to make drawings for castings, bearings, sprockets and things like that which were needed for the production of models. Everything revolved around whether Brenner's ideas could be put into practice. Although he was a brilliant designer, at that time many of his ideas were considered as pie in the sky. Our discussions were often rather noisy! However, anyone who knows Brenner will confirm that these arguments were productive and friendly.

Once the preparatory work had been reached a certain point, Herr Wallmeier — a remarkably talented metalworker with extraordinary practical skills — was called upon to bring a big sheet of steel. Brenner would then say. "I will now draw the machine with a piece of chalk exactly to scale on the sheet. You can then take the dimensions straight off the panel". You can imagine how accurate this method was with chalk marks that were 10 mm wide. For this reason a second "exact" drawing was made by Wallmeier, ably assisted by the youthful Bernhard Specht. Mr Specht, by the way, established an amazing worldwide reputation as a superb mechanic in the course of his career.

The development of the MDB

"We were covered in sweat and dust in the evening. However, we remained in the field and sat down in a circle on the bales of straw. August Claas then arrived on his bike. It was easy to recognise the bottle wrapped in his mackintosh on the back of the bike. He pulled his full cigarette case out of his pocket, to accompany the schnapps. The events of the day were talked over, with all the successes and failures. No stone was left unturned, and after everything had been mulled over properly,

the main points were summarised again. Everybody was assigned their specific tasks. Next morning the changes and improvements we had talked about were installed into the machine in the workshop. By the time the combine went back into use in the afternoon, it had already been brought up to the latest technical standard. This was the only way for us to make so much progress on the combine during a season".

Erich Harmening

Together they marked up another sheet of steel and traced an accurate drawing with a ruler, a pair of compasses and drawing pins on the 1:1 scale.

This was the basic design drawing for the first combine harvester to be built in Germany, the MDB. Once the basic design had been drawn up, models

Chief engineer Erich Harmening (left) meets chief mechanic Bernhard Specht and large farm proprietor Walter Haberland.

were then produced and painted red. After this the parts were manufactured and assembled to produce the complete machine. Corrections were required later on a frequent basis and the models were changed accordingly.

The proof testing started now. The prototype was driven by an electric motor via a reduction drive and power take off shaft. We carried out the functional tests with the machine stationary. For example, the cleaning had to be sorted out, the right paddle form had to be discovered, whilst the operating speed of the sieves and straw walkers had to be matched to the crop feed rate. A chaff sieve with suction air cleaning was even used for pre-cleaning. There were nei-

ther research data nor publications available at that time, so we had to work everything out ourselves, a time consuming process.

Once our functional tests and measurements had reached a satisfactory stage, a Lanz Bulldog fitted with elastic belts was hooked up in front and the machine run over a bad patch of land. Whenever something broke you strengthened it. Little by little, the machine became rugged enough for proper use.

Looking back on this period today, I am actually quite glad that nobody was watching us at that time. Later on, when we had progressed in our working

methods, August Claas was prepared to allow the owner of a competitive company to have a quick look inside our department. This person couldn't believe that this was all there was and expressed the opinion that we had withheld something from him. Our department must be three to five times the size, based on what he knew of our sales figures and his.

Field experience was translated into product improvements by chief engineer Erich Harmening with no delay. As a result, the development department was highly efficient.

Harmening, you're a lucky man!

Although the development department was very small, it worked very efficiently. This is made clear by a talk between Erich Harmening and a colleague who worked as chief engineer for a competitor:

"Harmening, old chap, we can talk frankly to one another. Your machines cause just as many problems as ours do from time to time. You have a great advantage over me. If something doesn't work, you just call August Claas on the telephone and tell him what needs to be changed. He contacts the development department, the models are changed on the spot and the improvement flows into your series the next day. The matter is dealt with in no time.

If I want to make an improvement and even if it means only a bolt has to be moved, I must make a written application and present a drawing with the modification. A year later, I hear from the parent company whether the application has been approved or rejected, because that's where the original set of drawings is stored. The earliest any changes can go into production is after one and a half or two years, if at all. With you it takes just two days and this is your strength".

Source:
"As combines came of age".
From "Agricultural equipment live" from an MEG-KTBL document dated 1981.

A SUPER IDEA

After the war Claas made the combine harvester into an every day tool thanks to the pull type Super model. More than 65 000 units of this successful machine had been sold by 1978.

Despite the order to produce material for the armaments industry in the Claas factory in Harsewinkel, work on development and testing of the combine harvester continued, albeit on a low-key basis. The first draft of the Super design is to be found in Dr Brenner's diary entry dated December 8th, 1942. Before the end of the war two prototypes were already running in Saxony and trial harvests were carried out in Westfalia with the new design.

The first edition of the Super was given with the model designation Mower-Thresher-Binder (MDB) Super. The engineers had realised that the limits in terms of performance were reached very quickly with the transverse crop flow of the MDB. It was not possible to increase the width beyond a certain point, and this led the designers to

Most farms couldn't get used to the idea of using combines. Here, the sheaves are fed manually into the combine at rest.

After the second world war, Claas achieved a major breakthrough with the Super pull type combine. Combine harvesting steadily eliminated the time consuming harvest methods of the past.

adopt a right angle flow principle, the crop being first transported sideways and then lengthways.

All thoughts about combines were discontinued in the chaos of 1945. Germany was totally on its knees and nobody was thinking about exporting combine harvesters at that time. In addition there was plenty of manpower with nothing to do so that labour saving harvesting systems were not very much in demand.

The English occupation forces confiscated one of the Super combines found in the factory and had it sent to England. This was considered a major affront to the people in the Harsewinkel plant. They were worried that the English would copy the design which had not been protected by patents at that time. However, the machine was just tested when it got to England. It would seem that the combine harvesting system was of so little interest

*Dr Brenner's diary entry dated December 8th,
1942 shows the general idea.*

on the other side of the English Channel that nobody thought it worthwhile to produce it there.

At a later date the test results came to light again and an import licence was made available. This means that the confiscated machine actually opened the door to exports to England.

By the early summer of 1946 the Harsewinkel factory was smaller than it had ever been. Then a bit of luck occurred, when an English officer ordered several combines to be sent to the Rhine valley. The harvest had to be gathered in urgently, and in the area around Jülich and Aachen there were neither threshing machines nor electricity. During the last weeks of the war the determined German resistance had led to highly destructive combat which had ruined everything, both in the towns as well as the villages.

This was the start of a most unusual campaign, in which three machines had first to be assembled or built from existing parts. The combine teams were given a training course, with two men allocated to each machine. The military government provided three Hanomag R40 tractors on the basis that diesel fuel would be obtained locally. Two chaff trailers were hitched behind each Super and one of these was filled with normal wear parts, whilst the second one was used by the team as a mobile hotel room complete with a layer of straw as bedding.

*The first machines were
still called MDB Type Super.*

Several combine harvesters were commandeered into an emergency harvest action in the Rhine valley. This provided valuable experience which was incorporated in the product development of the combine.

The journey from Harsewinkel into the Rhine valley was an adventure in itself. Almost all the bridges on the route had been destroyed and replaced by the very narrow temporary pontoon bridges. The teams were given a warm welcome when they arrived at the operation zone. The first priority was to thresh the wheat harvest, and the yields were very high by the standards of that time. Sugar beet had been planted the year before and this had been ploughed under, because it was impossible to harvest. This turned into a excellent fertiliser for the wheat crop.

Erich Harmening, who later became chief engineer, was responsible for this project. We quote from his report on the harvest in the Rhine valley: "Our Hanomag tractors had the habit of storming across the fields, even in first gear. They went much too fast. Our Super had no choice but to follow it and swallow everything, whether it wanted to or not. Obviously it rather frequently did not want to digest everything, so things broke or wrapping

occurred, along with other difficulties. It was an enormous challenge and we were able to gain a vast amount of experience which was extremely valuable to us, even if it was so hard won. We welded, reinforced, made steady improvements and this emergency harvest trial turned into a unique test bed. The Super was really toughened up and made capable of coping with the most difficult conditions around. The performance was raised to a standard which seemed inconceivable at the time. As a result of two years of harvest rescue trials in 1946 and 1947, we were able to export it to England in quite large numbers in 1948 as the highest performance combine in the world".

In common with its predecessor the crop was cut with the cutter bar located on the right hand side of the machine. It then flowed to the threshing drum via a conveyor angled slightly upwards. The drum took up the crop over a large width. This means that the ears were threshed on the rear side of the threshing drum. The straw was fed in from the front, enabling the threshing drum to concentrate on separating the ears and then feeding the material on through the combine. This purpose built flow method only worked fully in standing crops, and compromise settings had to be selected in laid crops.

The drum ejected the straw on to the straw walkers, whilst a capstan turned the stalks into the lengthways direction. The crop was then fed towards the back of the machine on the straw walkers. A paddle elevator transported the grain, the chaff and short straw on to the preparation pan, which then fed it to the cleaning system. The bagging platform was located on the machine's roof. Thanks to the frameless construction it was possible to load 750 kilograms onto the bagging platform. In common with the stationary threshing machines of that period, the crop was sorted into three different categories: first grade, fine and coarse.

Between 1945 and 1978, more than 65 000 Super combines were produced. During this 33 year period, Claas continued to improve the specifications. The grain tank became a standard feature in the later phase of production.

A straw baler was fitted as standard, whilst the chaff could also be collected in addition. The Super weighed 2 400 kg and had a cutting width of 2.10 m. A 35 hp tractor with power take-off was required for running the combine. The reel was taken off for road travel and the cutter bar folded up with a winch on the side of the machine. A pick-up was also available on an optional basis for threshing from the swath. According to the brochure this was called a "pick-up drum". Furthermore Claas offered equipment for stationary threshing in the barn.

At around the same time, auxiliary engines were added to the product range. This enabled the use of even smaller tractors for threshing. The dual engine option also had the advantage that the combine drive and the forward travel could be separated from one another. At that time PTO shafts were often not independently driven, although Dr Brenner had been loudly demanding this from the tractor makers on a frequent basis.

The Super family was subject to continuous development. As part of this process a grain tank came in place of the

The Super Junior was designed for small farms. A 25 hp tractor was all that was needed, whilst an auxiliary engine could be fitted optionally.

In 1953 a smaller version — the Super Junior — was put onto the market. This machine was designed for tractors with a rating of 25 hp. It had a cutting width of 1.65 m, the bagging platform was mounted on the side and the machine weighed just 1 960 kg.

Trailed or self-propelled?

After the initial boom, pull type combines were replaced little by a little by self-propelled machines during the sixties and seventies.

bagging platform. A chopper could be selected in place of the straw baler, and the latter was eliminated completely at a later date. It was even possible to harvest maize with this combine. A single row maize header could be fitted in place of the cutter bar. In those days it was normal practice to put the complete maize plant through the combine.

The introduction of hydraulics was a major step forward and this came about in 1959. First the Super and later the Junior could be equipped with a hydraulic control, and these models were named "Automatic". From then on the tractor driver could control the combine completely with a hydraulic control unit fitted on the fender. The cutting and reel heights could now easily be matched to the harvest conditions. At the same time a safety stop device was introduced. It operated a clutch via a cable which stopped the conveyor immediately when there was a risk of overload.

This legendary period of German combine harvesting history ended in 1978 with the last of the Super Automatic models. The story had begun back in 1942 with the diary entry of Dr Brenner. More than 65 000 machines of this type had by then been produced in Harsewinkel and sent to all corners of the world, where each of them made their own special contribution to easier, more efficient and profitable farming.

During the fifties pull type combine harvesters were the most common sight on fields in Germany. With prices of between 8 000 to 12 000 DM, this was a lower cost method of getting into combining than buying a self-propelled machine. By way of comparison: the self-propelled Europa had a similar output to the Super, but cost almost twice as much. That meant tying up nearly twice as much capital as a result of added components such as engine, transmission and running gear for a machine which was then used for just 120 to 150 hours per year.

The combine population was divided evenly into pull type and self-propelled combines up to 1960. After then, the pull type combine lost out steadily.

The tractors which were allocated to the trailed combines were often underpowered or were put into use for other tasks at short notice during the harvesting season. The auxiliary engine was an attempt to reduce the burden on the tractor. Many tractors only had three speeds and the independent PTO drive was far from being standard equipment. This made it impossible to fine tune the travel speed to changes in the harvesting conditions. As a result wrapping of the drum, blockages and overloading of the tractor were commonplace.

In comparison, the self-propelled combines featured a stepless transmission. In addition the SF of that period had 60 hp on board, so that meant it had plenty of power available. Farmers, machinery rings and contractors turned their attention increasingly to the self-propelled machines. Another advantage

was the front mounted cutter bar, particularly on small fields. None of the valuable crop was driven over or flattened when opening up the field. The driver had a much better view of the crop from his raised platform. It was also easier to go from one field to the next. The trailed combine had the drawback that the reel had to be removed each time, then replaced and the conveyor tensioned.

The sum of these advantages led to a steady increase in self-propelled machines. Up until 1960 the total combine population in Germany (50 000 units) was split equally between self-propelled and pull type combines. In 1960 the trend went clearly in favour of the self-propelled units (80%). In 1956, ten manufacturers in Germany offered pull type combines, and by 1966 only four were left. The number of models sank from sixteen to five. In the same period the number of self-propelled models increased from eight to thirty-seven.

The self-propelled combines also took over in other countries with small field sizes, such as Belgium. The picture was somewhat different in those countries with large sized farms. The pull type machines maintained their dominance in Denmark, for example. The USA with a population of some 1 million combines had a share of 80 per cent pull type machines.

In difficult harvesting conditions the tractor needed a well-matched transmission. The driver often had a tough job on his hands.

Claas stays faithful to the right angle crop flow

Unlike its competitors, Claas stuck to the right angle crop flow to the bitter end.

In the sixties and seventies it was not easy for Claas to compete with the Super combine design. They were increasingly up against machines that had a straight line crop flow and the self-propelled machines which appeared from 1953 were of course all designed with a straight line crop flow.

The Claas system did have significant advantages on difficult fields, because the machine ran in the tractor's tracks and so there was no pull to the side. In addition the PTO shaft angle was smaller, which meant that shaft breakage was a relatively rare occurrence when turning on headlands. On the other hand the combines with the straight line crop flow were quicker to set up. By swivelling the drawbar across, the machine could be quickly changed over from the travel position to the working position.

As it became increasingly difficult for Claas to defend the right angle flow system, the Garant was introduced in 1967 and this combine came with a straight line crop flow. However, this change in philosophy did not lead to the success that was hoped for. The trend towards self-propelled combines meant that the total market for pull type machines declined more and more.

Claas defended the right angle crop flow for a long while. Claas only brought out a straight line flow combine Garant when the era of the pull type combine was coming to a close.

THE GODFATHER OF THE
COMBINE HARVESTER IN GERMANY

Professor Brenner devoted himself to developing the
combine harvester for European harvesting conditions.

*Brenner had a reputation
as a brilliant designer
and made a major
contribution to combine
harvester development
in Germany.*

*Professor Brenner, Franz
Claas (centre) and
August Claas (right)
shared the common
goal of designing a
combine for harsh har-
vesting conditions.*

Brenner was born in Münchberg, a
town in Bavaria. His date of birth was
July 28th, 1899. He then spent his youth
as a son of a Bavarian civil servant in
Bayreuth. He studied mechanical
engineering at the Munich Technical
University between 1920 and 1924.

His professional career started in
Dessau at the Junkers aircraft factory.
At that time, aeronautical engineering
wasn't so attractive, with the result
that Brenner moved to the Technical
University in Stuttgart, in the agricultural equipment faculty. There he dealt
with sorting processes of seed corn in
wind currents and 1927 graduated to
PhD status as Doctor of Engineering.

After completion of these studies,
Brenner went to a company called Röber
based in Thuringia and developed a
seed cleaning system called "Petkus-
Hohenheim". He was still attracted by
the field of research and this explains
how he became an assistant of Professor Karl Vormfelde at the agricultural
university in Bonn-Poppelsdorf. Vormfelde was fascinated by combines and
had made his views public in an article
entitled "A new world order with the
combine harvester" published in the

VDI (German Engineers Association)
journal No. 6 in 1931. At first Brenner
dealt with basic research on threshing
and keep a close eye on the combines
imported from America. The results of
this work qualified him as a university
lecturer.

*Professor Brenner was always loyal to Claas
and was awarded a gold watch by August Claas
in recognition of his efforts after 25 years with
the company.*

Starting in 1930 Brenner advanced the
development of the combine in con-
junction with Claas. In 1949 he ac-
cepted a request from the Brunswick
Farm Research Institution to build up
the Institute for Agricultural Machinery
Research. He returned once more to
Claas in 1952. The completion of his
career saw him in the role of manager
of the Institute for Agricultural Engineering in Weihenstephan, part of
the Munich Technical High School.
Brenner died on December 8th, 1973.

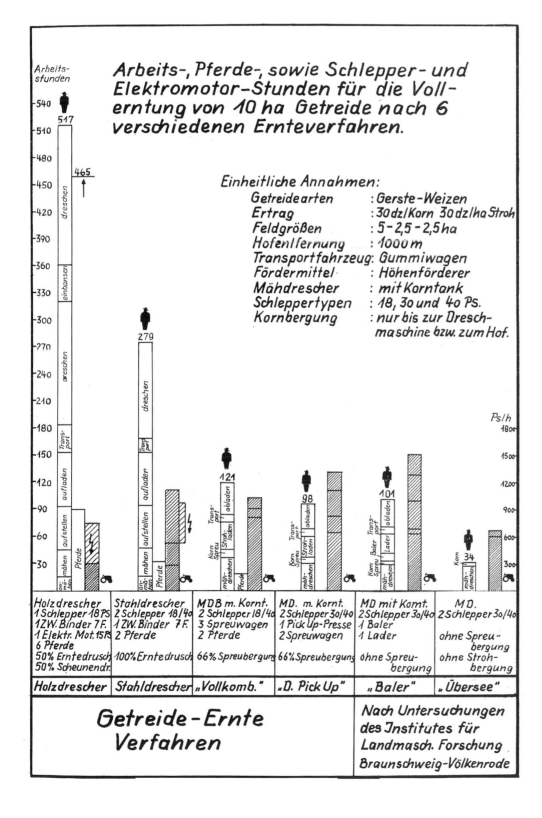

This chart from the Brunswick Institute demonstrates various stages of mechanisation. The first column with traditional harvesting takes 517 man hours to harvest 10 ha. On the right the combine just takes 34 man hours for the same area, providing the straw was not recuperated.

THE FIRST SELF-PROPELLED CLAAS COMBINE

Large farms needed more efficient combines and the response came in 1952 when the Hercules self-propelled combine was introduced. At this point Claas introduced a straight line crop flow.

Whilst the Super pull type combines were still being built in large numbers and continued development was taking place, the Harsewinkel team had set about designing a self-propelled combine. The self-propelled combine had a number of advantages. Here are three main ones:

1. Elimination of the labour intensive opening up of fields with the pull type combine.
2. Individual and stepless travel speed.
3. Higher work rates, particularly for big farms and contractors.

This development was backed strongly by August Claas personally. The Hercules was presented to the farming world on the occasion of his 65th birthday on December 15th, 1952. The company magazine "Der Knoter" (the knotter) reported on this event in the December 1952 edition: "The new Hercules combine with front mounted cutter bar has been given this name in view of its performance. Such performance can only come from a giant". Unfortunately nobody at Claas had noticed that the name "Hercules" was already protected by another company. In order to circumvent any legal disputes with an uncertain outcome, the name was changed to SF without further ado.

The SF was presented on the occasion of August Claas's 65th birthday.

This was an abbreviation for self-propelled in German (Selbstfahrer). The machine came into use on a wide range of farms for the first time in the 1953 harvest. The introduction of the self-propelled combine launched a

The self-propelled combine was called Hercules to emphasize its performance. It was renamed SF when problems cropped up with the registration of the name.

passionate debate in farming circles: was it economically viable to use a such expensive machine for such a short time period? Why couldn't the engine, transmission and chassis be adapted to carry out other work during the rest of the year? Weren't the more powerful tractors that were being developed able to obtain the same performances with the pull type combine? We all know today that the self-propelled combine did in fact succeed, a trend which repeated itself with forage harvesters later on.

Claas had decided that both large farms and contractors were to be considered as target groups for this machine, not just in Germany but also in export markets.

It was stressed at the introduction that this combine had a front mounted header. This is of course a design principle inherent to all self-propelled combines. August Claas wanted to make a special point of this, because it was necessary to defend the company's other machines with their right angled flow against other pull type combines which also had a straight line flow of crop through the machine.

The SF could be supplied either with a bagging platform or a grain tank. One unusual feature was that it was also offered without the mounted baler. A pick-up drum with spring tines could also be purchased as special equipment. The cutter bar had a width of 2.40 metres and was raised and lowered hydraulically. 3.00 metre to 4.20 metre wide cutter bars were available for export regions.

The reel also came with hydraulic height adjustment. The speed of the threshing drum and the travel speed were infinitely variable whilst the combine was moving. At first the adjustment was carried out via hand levers. Hydraulic adjustment followed very soon, however. The SF had a 1.25 metre wide threshing drum and four straw walkers. Initially the power was supplied by a 56 hp diesel or petrol engine which was located behind the bagging platform. Later models were then supplied with a 60 hp engine.

The SF was produced until 1963, giving it a ten year production run. Later models such as the Matador, Protector, Senator and Mercator were based on much the same design.

COMBINE HARVESTER
AND IMPLEMENT CARRIER IN ONE

The "Piggy-back" or "Huckepack" was a prime mover
that could be turned into a tractor or implement carrier.

*The forerunner of the
Claas Xerion did not meet
the company's sales
expectations. There was
not enough engine power
and simple couplings for
hydraulic and electrical
circuits or the PTO shaft
were not available.*

The SF self-propelled combine was
clearly designed for the larger sized
farming businesses, machinery rings and
contractors of the fifties. All that was
missing now was a self-propelled combine which smaller farmers could afford
to buy. The question was whether they
could really justify the luxury of using
the whole chassis with engine and
transmissions just for a few weeks
a year during the harvest and have all
this expensive gear lying around in
the machine shed.

As usual the inventors at Claas applied
their minds to this issue and came up
with a surprising answer once again.
The Claas "Huckepack" was displayed at
the 44th DLG exhibition from September
9th to 14th, 1956 in Hanover, much to
the amazement of the whole farming
community. This "Piggy-back" machine
was a self-ropelled combine which could
be modified into an implement carrier
outside of the harvest season. This
machine went in production in 1957.

*The machine for every task
on the small farm. The
"Piggy-back" could thresh
the cereals harvest and
spend the rest of the year
working as an implement
carrier.*

This hybrid machine had a 2.10 metre
wide cutter bar. The threshing drum
was 800 mm in width and three straw
walkers provided the secondary grain
separation. The grain was filled into bags
on the bagging stand, as was common
practice at that time. For the same reason, a straw baler was also mounted at
the rear of the combine.

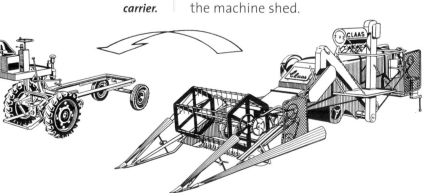

The driver's position was an unusual feature of this machine. When combining, the operator sat on the right in travel direction. Since the bagging stand was on the left, you drove always to the right which meant that the driver had to peer over the cutter bar to be able to keep an eye on the edge of the standing crop on the other side. To be fair, this was not tragic in view of the 2.10 metre cutting width, but it certainly took a bit of getting used to.

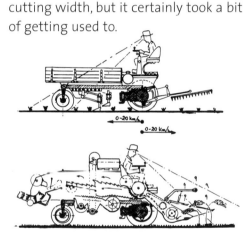

Another unusual feature was the dual engine layout. The "prime mover" was driven by a 12 hp diesel engine. The combine harvester unit had an industrial Volkswagen engine of its own with 34 hp, the same as the one that powered the VW Beetle at that time.

The transmission of the prime mover offered five forward speeds and one reverse gear. A reverser provided the same speed in both travel directions. This was necessary because the machine ran forwards when threshing and backwards in the tractor mode. An additional creeper gear was available for implement carrier work.

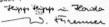

Institut für angewandte
Landmaschinentechnik

Weihenstephan   Weihenstephan,
                             5. Juli 1956

An die Firma
Gebr. C l a a s
Maschinenfabrik
H a r s e w i n k e l
Westfalen

Betrifft: Selbstfahrer-Huckepack

In postwendender Beantwortung Ihrer Anfrage vom 3.7., teile ich Ihnen mit, daß ich das neue Wort „Huckepack" – wie ich schon Herrn August Claas telephonisch mitgeteilt habe – für sehr gut halte. Wenn dieses Wort dann noch entsprechend mit Propaganda unterbaut wird, so wird es sich sicher sehr gut machen und einprägen.

Das Wort Huckepack ist zwar nicht international verständlich, aber es ist anzunehmen, daß die Franzosen und Engländer sich an so ein Wort heute auch ganz gerne gewöhnen und es irgendwie originell finden a la Auspuff-Topff (seligen Andenkens) oder Pumpernickel!

Ich würde also dieses Wort auch in die englischen und französischen Prospekte aufnehmen und nicht verändern.

Mit freundlichen Grüßen und den besten Wünschen für den neuen „Huckpack".

Dismantling the threshing unit and converting the chassis into an implement carrier took two men approximately 30 minutes. Among other things the driver's seat had to be refitted on the opposite side of the steering wheel.

The implement carrier had a chassis made of a pair of parallel tubes running the length of the machine. All commonly available tractor implements could be fitted to the frame between the axles and operated hydraulically. In addition, a load platform could be fitted for transport work. There were three point hydraulics behind the drive axle, so all normal equipment could be attached. In addition, the vehicle had a standard power take-off.

Professor Brenner explains in this letter to Claas that he favours the new name "Huckepack", despite the fact that it means nothing in other languages. He requests that the name be used in French and English literature and expects it to be adopted as other words have been, once people get used to them.

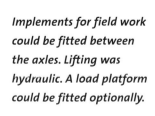

Implements for field work could be fitted between the axles. Lifting was hydraulic. A load platform could be fitted optionally.

Claas achieved the long awaited breakthrough with the Europa and Columbus combines. They were sold in vast numbers.

The crop was still being packed into sacks on a large number of farms. Therefore the Europa was delivered either with a bagging stand or a grain tank. A novelty was the straw chopper behind the straw baler, so the farmer could choose between baling or chopping. The chopper was offered on its own without the straw baler later on. For the first time the leaflet quantifies the performance increase resulting from laying the straw in a swath with 5 to 10% versus baling it.

The small combine had a hydraulic cutter bar and reel adjustment. In addition, the drive variator was controlled hydraulically. A 45 hp diesel engine drove the machine, with the option of a 38 hp VW industrial engine.

The threshing system worked with a 800 mm wide threshing drum with a diameter of 450 mm. The drum speed could be set in a range from 620 to 1380 rpm by changing the pulleys. The disawning system was also new and patented by Claas. The secondary separation was carried out via three straw walkers. The Europa stayed in production to 1968.

Monsieur Jean-Marc Pol, a farmer in the north of France, loves old machines. He bought this Columbus with the serial number 5981, produced in 1963, and considers it one of his treasures. He has other more recent Claas products in his fleet to carry out his contracting business: five combines, three Jaguar forage harvesters and two Quadrant big balers. The Columbus is only used for very small fields. In addition, it has become part of tradition to harvest the last area with this classic combine. Only then is it time for harvest thanksgiving.

A smaller brother with the name of Columbus was built up until 1970. The specifications of the two models were very much alike. The Columbus cutter bar was only 1.80 metre wide. A 29 hp VW industrial engine was fitted with an optional 34 hp diesel engine. Otherwise the insides were very similar. The threshing drum specifications were identical with 450 mm diameter and 800 mm width. Three straw walkers separated the remaining grains from the straw.

The Europa and Columbus became the best-selling machines of all time for Claas. Altogether the company built more than 64 000 units.

A gap opened up between the Matador and the smaller Columbus/Europa models. This gap was closed with the Mercur, which was launched in 1963. The Europa and Columbus were three straw walkers combines with 800 mm threshing drum width, whilst the Matador featured 1 250 threshing drum width and four straw walkers. The Mercur was also a four straw walker machine with a narrower drum width of 1 060 mm, which made it an ideal fit between the two other ranges. The choice of the other main specifications was also designed to fill the gap.

The combines were extremely up to date by contemporary standards. Special features included hydraulic cutter bar and reel control. The drive variator was also hydraulically controlled.

THE ENTRY OF EVEN BIGGER COMBINES

The Matador standard and Gigant continued the advance of the big combine harvester era. Cutter bars of up to 6 metres were now featured.

The Matador was developed with large farms and contractors in mind. Combining had still not established itself fully in 1960. The sheaves in the background prove that a lot of farms still preferred to work with the reaper and threshing machine.

The Matador was offered with a cutter bar width of up to six metres. For road travel a cutter bar trailer was now required for cutting widths that exceeded three metres.

As a result of the economic miracle in post-war Germany, more and more people were moving from the farming sector into industry. As a result, larger farms in particular had to look for more productive machinery and adopt more efficient working methods to make up. The SF, which had been built as a top of the line machine from 1953, was no longer able to fully meet these demands. By 1971 the time had come to a introduce a successor.

The replacement came in the form of the Matador which was offered in two different versions. Since the machines were enormous by contemporary standards, the larger model was called „Gigant" or Giant. The smaller model was called Standard. The farm economic advisers worked out that the Matador was a financially viable investment for farms with at least 40 ha of cereals to harvest.

The cutter bar range went from 8.5 to 20 feet (2.60 metres to 6.00 metres). Both the Matador models were equipped with a 1.25 metre threshing drum width and a diameter of 450 mm, which was typical of Claas combines. The straw walker area on the Gigant was 4.5 m², which made it half a square-metre larger than on the Standard. The grain tank volume was also somewhat larger (2 690 litres with a tank hopper extension) on the Gigant versus the Standard (1 700 litres).

For the first time the grain tank had now become part of the standard specifications. The bagging platform was still offered on an optional basis, and even came with a lower price tag.

The straw baler was also transferred to the list of options at this point. The engine was fitted behind the grain tank, as was standard practice on the larger Claas combines. The Matador Standard was powered with a 62 hp diesel engine, whilst the Gigant had an 87 hp six cylinder engine installed.

In June 1963 the Gigant was certified in a test programme organised by the DLG in Germany. The throughput of the combine was rated at 3.3 tons per hour on average. At travel speeds varying from 2.0 to 4.5 km the German test centre reached a work rate of 0.5 to 1.1 ha/h. The average fuel consumption amounted to 9.6 litres per hour. In the test report special mention is made of the fact that the combine with a grain tank can be operated by just one person. For the version with the bagging platform, the test personnel concluded that three to four people were necessary. The price of the combine harvester at that time was 34 130 DM.

In 1962 Claas reached a statistical landmark. The company celebrated the production of the 100 000th combine during the 47th DLG exhibition. The honour was given to a Matador combine. August Claas donated this machine to the Agriculture Ministry of the north German state of Schleswig-Holstein, with the laudable intention of relieving the hardship caused by the flood catastrophe that had wrought havoc in the region. The combine was handed over to a machinery ring Ülvesbüllerkoog.

A large number of machines were exported, and the wider cutter bars came into their own in these conditions. This Matador with 6 metre working width really was a giant by contemporary standards.

The maize harvest was increasing in importance in Germany. New varieties with early ripening meant that grain maize could be cultivated in less than ideal climatic conditions.

With the introduction of the Matador to the production lines, the assembly procedures for the big self-propelled machines were changed. The machines were now towed sideways down the line, pulled by an under floor conveyor. The idea was to enable materials handling equipment to cross the production line wherever needed. Claas also broke

Claas offered hydraulic power-assisted steering to make handling easier on this heavy machine.

new ground in German farm equipment manufacturing by installing a full-scale test bed at the end of the assembly line consisting of three testing stations.

The assembly line for the pull type combines and the two small Europa and Columbus self-propelled machines was also driven by an under floor conveyor chain. These machines were still pulled along in travel direction. A third assembly line went into operation in Harsewinkel for the 1964 season.

The combine business was booming still and 100 machines a day were leaving the factory. That meant one machine every 5.7 minutes. Approximately two-thirds of the production was exported. The Claas market share in Europe was around 40 per cent.

Gigantic — 35 years in service

This Claas Matador Gigant is not destined for the scrap heap, even if it has reached an advanced age.

The reason that Norbert Prossenitsch, an Austrian farmer, can't imagine letting go his Matador Gigant is maybe their shared year of birth. The combine with the serial number 9590 was built in 1965, the same year that Mr Prossenitsch was born. Sure it would be nice to have a new combine, he thinks, but why sell the Gigant whilst it's still going strong?

Before the pair of them met up in 1973 the Gigant had been working for two contractors. In the space of eight years, it had it accumulated around 1 000 ha. Since then the combine has clocked up 2 500 ha and 3 000 operating hours. The arable farm belonging to the family is located near the Slovakian border, and there are 30 to 35 ha of cereals to

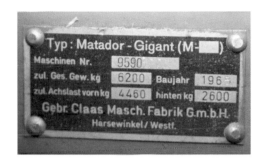

be harvested along with a few acres of peas each year. In addition Mr Prossenitsch Senior has also harvested up to 20 ha of cereals in the neighbourhood on a contract basis.

Father and son have come to an agreement on division of labour: dad drives, his son repairs. However, the combine has revealed no serious weaknesses to date. A full overhaul at the start has

Both the Matador Gigant with serial number 9590 and its owner, Norbert Prossenitsch, saw the light of day in 1965.

The combine threshes 30 to 35 ha of cereals each year on the family farm in Austria. To date, the Matador has clocked up 2 500 ha and 3 000 operating hours.

In such a long combine life it is not unusual to have to repair the discharge auger. The slight bend in it was resolved by shortening the whole tube. The discharge height is now inadequate for big trailers, but even this problem is overcome by laying planks under the left front wheel or by judicious selection of the discharge point.

been followed simply by replacement of wear items. And the largest repairs of any note have been a complete overhaul of the cutter bar and replacement of variator discs. In addition the intake chain plus the drive had to be renewed. Second-hand parts are frequently used in order to keep the costs down. In one case the drive of the rev indicator for the drum was fixed using a piece of elastic from a pair of trousers.

"It runs perfectly considering its age," says Norbert Prossenitsch, commenting on the condition of his combine and he hopes that the two of them will stay together for another ten years at least. In his opinion it is the lowest cost way of harvesting his small area of cereals.

Norbert Prossenitsch in action with his Gigant. The Austrian farmer hopes that his combine will keep going for another ten years.

It doesn't really matter that the Matador Gigant starts its working day later than more modern combines. It is also of little consequence that the combine has to stop an hour earlier, because as soon as the straw becomes damp the risk of drum wrapping increases. During dry summer days the Matador is still running well after sunset and is able to exceed its average daily work rate of six to seven hectares by a wide margin.

The only thing that can stop it is running out of fuel. From time to time, in the heat of battle, the operator has been known to forget to fill up the machine in time. "It happened once around midnight, the engine just stalled", the Prossenitsch team recalls fondly.

SUDDENLY APPEARANCES COUNT

The introduction of the Senator was the occasion for Claas to present a new design and the leaf green colour scheme.

The main considerations in designing a combine up to the siexties were firstly improved performance along with functional characteristics. In view of this, the external appearance of the machines was only of secondary importance. The Senator was the first combine from Claas that was influenced visibly by a designer.

The combine was introduced to the market in 1966 and featured large outer panels and covers. These gave the Senator a distinctive and elegant appearance. The Claas logo was redesigned and the machines were painted in the leaf green colour which is still a key characteristic of all Claas products today. In addition more and more attention had been giv-en to simpler machine operation.

The Senator was delivered with 3.00 metre to 4.20 metre cutter bars. It had four straw walkers and was driven by a 105 hp diesel engine. The grain tank had a capacity of 3 200 litres and the bagging stand had finally been put to rest, never to return. Claas offered a

The Senator's large side panels and covers really stood out. The leaf green paint scheme was also new.

It was almost impossible to separate the Mercator from the Senator from outside. The Mercator family replaced the Senator and Protector models at a later stage. Each model then had its own model number.

variety of options including pick-up
drums, maize headers and pickers as
well as a straw chopper and a cab.
Claas had made a practice of giving
every machine a name of its own. That
often led to a model being assigned a
completely different name although
the specification differences were min-
imal. It was only later that numbers
were allocated to the names to classify
size differences in the same family.

Pickers, maize cutters and pick-up drums were all available alongside the cereals cutter bars. The fully enclosed discharge auger is an outstanding design feature.

Later, the company gave up individual model names and the Senator and Protector were phased out. The Mercator was subject to a steady improvement programme which included expanding the range and these models were distinguished by an additional two-digit model number like Mercator 50, 60 and so on. In the autumn of 1981 the Mercator 50, 60 and 75 appeared in the German price list for the last time.

The new design didn't just cover the looks of the machine. The combine was much easier to operate, as the clean layout of the driver's platform shows.

In 1968 a smaller machine was added and was christened Protector. It had four and six cylinder engines starting with 68 hp and came with cutter bars from 2.60 metres in width.

That same year, a Senator with remote controlled steering was displayed at the German DLG agricultural equipment exhibition. This innovation was born of the durability testing cycles, in which the combine was run for an extended period on an obstacle course. This was so tough on the drivers that an automatic steering system was created. The driverless combine is one of the inventions that still has not caught on, even to this day.

Cosmos, Consul & Co.

Once the Columbus had conquered the family farms, it was succeeded by the more modern Consul, Cosmos, Comet and Corsar combine models.

The new range that Claas put onto the market at the end of the sixties was aimed at the mechanisation of small farms. The external appearance of these combines was quite unlike that of their predecessors.

As the sixties came to end, the trend in favour of big combines was gathering pace. Parallel to this trend, there was still plenty of demand for small machines which enabled traditional farmers to mechanise their harvest. Contractors had still not made many inroads with their large scale equipment into regions with small plots and hills. The cheaper pull type com-

bines also had difficulties operating in such conditions. These farmers had little choice but to buy their own small self-propelled combine. Many farmers had already invested in a Columbus or Europa during the previous years, but the machines had come technically and visually rather long in the tooth, so that the time was ripe for successors.

The new machines with the side mounted engines all featured the new styling introduced with the Senator, Protector and Mercator. The Consul and the Cosmos were introduced in 1967 and the Comet and Corsar followed onto the German market a year later. They all had different names, despite the fact that they were all derived from the same basic design.

All the models had the familiar 450 mm diameter Claas threshing drum. The Consul had a 1.06 metre drum width, the other models 0.80 m. As a result the Consul was a four straw walker com-

The four straw walker Consul was the largest model. The maize picker took over from the maize cutter bar.

bine. The other models worked with three straw walkers. Apart from this, the models were differentiated by cutting width: 1.80 to 3.0 metre cutter bars were available.

There were also different engine choices. The VW industrial engine with 29 or 38 hp was still in the range, whilst the Consul was offered with a 68 hp diesel engine. The grain tank with capacities between 1 350 and 2 000 litres had

taken over from the bagging stand for good, although a sack filling device for the discharge auger could still be purchased.

A new maize picker replaced the maize cutter bar, which was still prevalent at this time. In addition, a cab could be fitted on an optional basis. Pictures which show these machines with a cab are nevertheless a rarity.

The combines were an attractive proposition for farms with small field sizes versus pull type combines. There were also plenty of regions in which the farmers had to invest in their own small combines, because contractors had not yet established themselves with their big machines.

FROM PRESSED STEEL SEATS
TO THE COCKPIT

The driver of early combine harvesters had to put up with dust, noise and discomfort. The introduction of cabs led to steady improvements in comfort.

Operator and driver comfort were totally absent from early combine harvesters.

The driver of the SF was not seated very comfortably either. Cutter bar and reel control were, however, hydraulically operated.

The operator of the original MDB had plenty of reasons to complain about the level of comfort. In fact comfort was virtually non-existent. The seat was no more than a steel dish: from here the cutting height as well as the reel position were adjusted by physical strength via big hand levers. His colleague on the Bulldog tractor wasn't much better off either. Increased comfort was provided only by adding a cushion of chaff or chopped straw onto the metal seat.

The later models on the so called "Super Line" did away with the combine operator. The operator's platform became of interest again on the SF self-propelled combine. This was still equipped very sparingly indeed. The driver's seat was neither sprung nor adjustable, although by now the cutter bar and reel height were both set hydraulically. The same

applied to the drum speed adjustment. The travel speed could be adjusted steplessly with a belt variator. The instrumentation was confined to an hour meter plus water temperature and engine oil pressure gauges. The threshing drum rev counter rounded off the available equipment.

The view onto the cutter bar was far superior on the self propelled combines, compared with the pull type models. Ergonomic considerations had, however, not yet begun to increase in importance.

During the following years the operator's compartment was steadily improved. The driver's seat was equipped with a parallelogram suspension and was made height adjustable by means of two bolts. As of 1963 power steering was added for the Matador on an optional basis, appearing in the price list as hydraulic steering assistance. The leaflet describes this as follows: "Without the straw baler the Matador is easy to steer. The additional load on the rear axle caused by the straw baler can be compensated for with the highly effective hydraulic steering assistance. Then you can steer this big machine at the lowest speed like a light passenger car".

The operating and control functions were grouped together. The driver had all the main controls within easy reach and could check things at a glance.

The operator's compartment of the smaller models like Europa, Mercur etc. were kept just as simple. There was, however, much less space and the driver was seated to one side in rather cramped conditions. Visibility was impaired and the driver was perpetually surrounded by clouds of dust.

A sun shade is found for the first time in the German accessories price list for the operator's compartment from the year 1965. We can assume that this awning was supplied earlier in warmer countries such as Australia, Spain, Italy, Africa and New Zealand.

The first cabs appear in the 1967 price list. They were available on the Senator and Mercator models. Originally they ran under the name "driver's housing".

They weren't designed to reduce exposure to dust. Instead their aim appears to be to afford added protection for the driver against cold and damp in the maize harvest late in the season.

Driver comfort continued to advance step by step as demonstrated by the Dominator 80 in 1970. The operator's platform had been tidied up considerably and was more spacious in comparison with the previous models. This machine was the first Claas combine to have a hydrostatic ground drive. Within the following years a function monitor was introduced that supervised the rotation speeds of the feed housing, straw walker, grain and returns elevator as well as the straw chopper rpm. An electronic throughput control reported to the driver if the straw walker or sieve box losses exceeded the limit. The driver had at last a system that enabled the travel speed to be varied so as to get the best performance. The earlier cab was superseded by the comfort cab which had heating and ventilation.

The Dominator operator's platform was clearly laid out and more spacious than the previous models. The engine was located right behind the driver, and was a source of heat and noise.

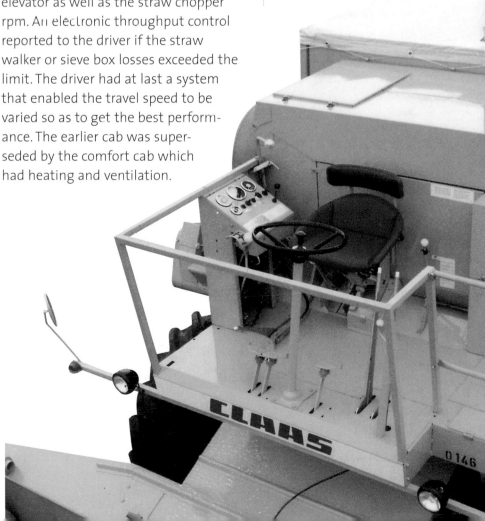

The sun canopy, which made its debut in 1965, brought a bit of shade. It was sold mainly in export regions of southern Europe, Africa, Australia etc.

The add-onprice for the cab was up to 8 000 DM, and there was as usual a lot of debate on whether it was worth the extra. The lack of adequate ventilation or air conditioning meant that the cab would heat up so the driver ended up opening all the doors and windows

anyway. As a result, there was as much dust flying around as beforehand. Simple fans (from Gassner, for instance) or dust blowers (e.g. on the Dominator 80) were offered as an alternative to the cab. The dust problem could be partially alleviated, but it was still only an incomplete solution.

The driver's cab increasingly became a must. With the Dominator "6" models the cab became standard equipment. For the first time, the cab wasn't a bolt-on version, but was an integral part of the combine. The driver finally had a seat comparable to those fitted to lorries. The drive information unit in front of the operator was located in the field of vision with all the information necessary to operating the machine

The first Claas combines available with a cab were the Senator and Mercator. It was especially sought after in maize producing regions, where harvesting took place in the damp late autumn season.

readily available. Increased control elements were vital now, since the cab isolated the driver from what was going on around the machine.

As combines got bigger and output went up, the driver increasingly became the limiting factor in terms of getting higher work rates. It turned out that the built-in potential was often not fully utilised. The driver needed more information to set up the machine correctly and to select the best forward speed. The operator also needed to feel at home in the working environment and stay alert during the long working day in the harvest.

During the seventies, only a few combines were fitted with a cab. Many farmers felt that the additional 8 000 DM was too much for the brief harvesting period.

The introduction of the multifunction control lever modelled on the joy stick principle which was introduced on the "8" series Dominator in 1985 was a major step in terms of improving driver control. Now he — or sometimes she — had the essential operating functions in one hand. An on-board information unit now provided operating hour and service interval data, travel speed and rpm of various shafts plus lots of other things. Air conditioning was now offered along with heating.

When the Lexion 480 was launched with the Vista cab, Claas had designed the nearest thing to a fully fledged cockpit. Electronics had taken over the main control and monitoring functions completely. Cebis (Claas Electronic On-Board Information System) provides the driver with everything needed concerning the operating parameters of the combine. The basic machine set up was also built in to the system. Threshing drum speed, concave spacing, sieve box opening and fan speeds are automatically set, using preset values arrived at from lengthy experience.

The combine set up and monitoring is carried out by the on-board computer based on preset values. All controls are grouped in the multifunction control lever.

These values can be overridden by the driver and stored separately. Cebis measures the area harvested, the crop volume and grain humidity. This data can be both printed out and filed on a chip card for analysis on the farm's office computer. Cebis also makes it possible to meter the yields and this is the entry point for farmers into precision farming.

Driver effort was further reduced with the introduction of the Laser Pilot. This is an automatic steering for working in cereals. With the steering function taken care of, the driver can then concentrate fully on fine-tuning the machine and, most importantly, keeping the combine

running at the highest speed across the field. This is a major contributor to higher throughput and brings the user closer to getting the maximum output from the combine all the time.

The Laser Pilot made it possible to run along the edge of the crop. It steers the combine automatically.

The operating compartment has evolved steadily into a cockpit. This is an essential step in helping the driver to generate the best output from the combine all day long.

COMPACT COMBINES FOR SMALL FARMS

Claas designed a completely new small combine called "Compact".

The Consul, Cosmos, Comet and Corsar had been on the market for just three years when Claas surprised everyone with two completely new combines in the same output category. The Compact 20 and 25 rounded off the product range beneath the Dominator 80, which was launched at the same time.

Both machines were purpose-built small combines, in contrast with previous machines that had always been derived from larger ones. The conse-

quence of this top-down approach was that the production of the small combines was frequently too expensive and they generated less profit. The Compact was supposed to be the right answer for economic combine harvesting in areas with small, irregular formed fields. At its introduction, the

Compact range was proclaimed as being small but with amazingly high performance for its size. In many areas these combines were indeed a match for the bigger models, whilst still being affordable for smaller farmers.

The Compact 20 had a cutter bar width of 1.72 metres. The three straw walker machine had a 0.58 metre wide threshing drum and was driven by a 24 hp VW industrial engine. The grain tank could hold 850 litres. The bigger Compact 25 came with a 2.10 metre cutter bar and was also fitted with a VW industrial engine, featuring an output of 34 hp. The threshing drum was 0.96 metres wide and the grain tank of this five straw walker combine had a capacity of 1 100 litres.

In the following years the range was extended with the introduction of the Compact 30 combine. When this machine appeared in the price list for the last time in 1981, it was equipped with a 1 900 litre grain tank and motive power was provided by a 53 hp diesel engine.

Claas presented the Compact range in 1970 with the aim of offering an economic combine to smaller farms.
The combines were based on a completely new design concept. In prior years, small combines had usually been derived from larger models, so their production cost was inevitably too high.

An interesting detail on these machines is the fold-up straw cowl, which was designed so that the driver could easily check and clean the straw walkers and sieves despite the low overall height of the combine.

The Claas jumbo

Claas exhibited a design project on the 1970 DLG exhibition in Germany. However, the futuristic looking combine did not make it onto the production line.

The project study was aimed at getting a maximum number of combines onto rail wagons within the rail tunnel profile. Its unusual shape led it to being nicknamed by the Claas fraternity as the "dustbin".

The design study was a popular meeting point on the DLG exhibition at Cologne.

The work of development departments is normally carried out in secrecy and behind locked doors. The competition is not supposed to find out about the projects the company is working on until the very last moment. This is true of all companies involved in the development of products for industrial markets. Nonetheless it sometimes makes sense to present the public with a design study to test the acceptance of the target group before continuing with the project.

This is the background to the presentation by Claas of a combine project study which was revealed at the 51st DLG exhibition which took place at Cologne in 1970. The study was unlike anything that been seen before at Claas, with a distinctive rounded shape to the panels, which made it look very futuristic. The engineers had set themselves the task of packing as many combines as possible within the limits of the railway's tunnel profile for efficient rail shipment. There

This cartoon from "Der Knoter" has as a caption: "The magnet of the exhibition, our new super combine, was permanently surrounded by hundreds of curious people and purchasers". A competitor is saying "Don't believe a word of it, they've pumped it up".

was only sparse information available on this combine and no specifications were released. The machine stood on the exhibition behind a barrier and could only be judged from a distance. The grain storage was another unusual feature, with saddle tanks either side of the combine.

In the 3/1970 issue of the company magazine "Der Knoter" there was a report on the exhibition. The Claas stand was a particularly popular meeting place. Again and again visitors were overheard saying "We'll meet up at the fat Claas combine". The large combine was indeed permanently surrounded by farmers who spent lots of time discussing the unusual features of the machine. This combine shape never went into series production. Instead the Dominator 80 was introduced to the market in the 1970/71 season, the forerunner of the outstandingly successful Dominator family.

ENDURANCE TESTING IN RICE

Rice harvesting places very heavy demands on a combine. Claas shipped its first combines to Italian rice fields way back in the thirties.

August Claas always followed the objective of developing machines for universal use. The toughest challenge for a combine harvester is the rice harvest. August Claas and his engineer Wallmeier travelled to Italy in the early 1930ies to set up the first combining trials in rice. A photo is still in existence showing a special front mounted header wrapped around a Fiat belt drive tractor, working on a field near Vercelli in the Po valley.

The Super and the Junior combines were also put into service in Vercelli. According to Claas, the right angled crop flow performed outstandingly well in the extremely arduous har-

vesting conditions. Unlike the pull type combines with a straight line crop flow, the Claas combines followed the tractor's path and were easier to pull. The shorter drawbar also made turning on the headlands easier.

The first self-propelled combines also made their way to Italy. Later the Europa was put into the field. In the years that followed, virtually all of the larger combine models were modified to make them suitable for rice harvesting. The rice machine is adapted from the conventional combine unit, because the majority of components which provide good results in the wheat harvest are just as good in rice.

August Claas realised early on that the combine needed to be a versatile harvesting machine.

His combines had to withstand the tough tests in rice. The first combines were put into service in the Po valley.

The tracks instead of wheels are the most noticeable characteristic of combines in the rice harvest. This enables harvesting over soft ground.

Special equipment is necessary to separate the grains gently and feed them to the grain tank without damage.

The crop has a high silica content and this leads to significantly higher wear and tear. The intake auger flights, the grain and returns auger plus the feed to the grain tank are all coated with hard wearing material. Threshing is done with a spiked tooth threshing

drum and concave. The tines are made of extra strength steel and bolted individually to the drum and concave.

The cutter bar is only changed slightly for the rice harvest. The normal crop separators are replaced with special rice ones. In some regions, a special cutter bar is called for with counter-moving knives and no fingers.

Half tracks are fitted in place of wheels for operation over soft paddy fields. These have a larger footprint and reduce the ground pressure. There are a lot of regions in which the rice combines are also employed for wheat and other cereals harvests. In such cases, the half tracks are removed and replaced by tyres, and the tine threshing drum and concave unit is also swapped over for a normal one.

THE TIGER IN THE RICE PADDY

Claas starts up in Asia with the Crop Tiger rice combine.

Claas started to become interested in the Chinese market in the 1980ies. This huge country with a low level of mechanisation seemed to offer enormous sales possibilities. There were many unresolved questions: what does Chinese farming need, what are the prevailing conditions like? The result of intensive research was that the country requires small combines first and foremost.

The bulk of Crop Tiger combines is running in India. The grain tank is often emptied into sacks at the edge of the field.

In 1987, Claas entered into a cooperation agreement with Chinese partners. The Crop Tiger was developed and tested in Harsewinkel. Further tests were then carried out in China and the first ten combines were put into operation in 1989. This ambitious project suffered a major setback when the Chinese partners decided to pull out.

Claas was determined to continue working on the development, and went out in search of another economically stable country. This turned out to be

India and a joint venture was subsequently signed with Escorts Limited, a multi-faceted Indian company group. The Crop Tiger was modified to suit the local conditions and adapted to suit the level of manufacturing technology in India. The links between Escorts Claas Limited and Claas in Harsewinkel intensified steadily over the coming years. For this reason, further development and trials were passed over to the company in Faridabad, which is about 20 km south of Delhi. This know-how transfer enabled the quality standards to be brought up to the same level as in other Claas factories.

The Crop Tiger has mostly been put into service in the south of India, with exports taking place to countries as wide apart as South Korea, Egypt and Thai-

land, to name just a few. The machine is designed around a right angled rotor. Whilst it was originally conceived for rice harvesting, it can also thresh cereals after changing some parts. The threshing and separation is mounted at 90° to the travel direction with the crop entering the threshing drum at right angles. The straw is then fed directly to the axial separation drum. The two drums make up a single unit, with threshing and separation taking place from right to left. This explains the intake auger layout, which feeds the crop to the right hand side, unlike the more common central feeding. This is no problem in view of the cutting width of just 2.10 metres. The straw then drops out of the machine on the left, although it can also be trans-ported on a conveyor belt to the rear centre, where it lays a swath together with the material coming from the sieve box.

The Crop Tiger comes with a belt drive for harvesting rice. In the meantime a wheeled version has been developed in India. The combine was designed with a grain tank as standard, although the contents are often emptied into sacks at the end of the field or discharged onto a sheet from where the crop is placed in sacks directly. A bagging station wasn't feasible on the Crop Tiger, because of its high output plus the lack of space for several bagging operators and the filled sacks on this extremely compact machine.

The compact machine is used predominantly in rice. It can also harvest cereals, if so required.

The 170 hp Dominator 100 threshing oil seed rape from the swath. The engine position right behind the driver was a characteristic of the Dominator combines. It enabled a shorter drive to the threshing drum.

The cab boosted the comfort on the Dominator combines. However, this could only be enjoyed with air conditioning fitted, so the doors and windows could be kept closed.

Every year, improvements flowed into the production runs. Yields were progressing steadily as a result of new hybrids and improvements in farming methods. This pushed existing technology in terms of threshing and separation to its limits. The straw walkers were the most critical part of the machines. As a consequence, Claas came up with the intensive separation system in 1975.

Depending on the length of the straw walkers, either one or two controlled tines were mounted on top of the straw walkers. They dug into the mat of straw and aerated it, so that the straw could flow more freely. This meant that the loose grains could drop onto the returns floor beneath the straw walkers unimpeded by the straw. Claas fitted the intensive separation system to both the Dominator models as well as the

larger Mercator. The models fitted with intensive separation were identified by the suffix 5 in place of the previous 0.

A survey of the chambers of agriculture and other associations in 1977 showed to what extent the customers were satisfied with the Dominator series. The Dominator 80 still suffered from some teething troubles during the first years. Of 84 owners sampled, 18 weren't satisfied with their purchase. They complained about too many repairs and the high costs associated with this lack of reliability. Many users claimed that the machine design was marketed prematurely.

Many problems were solved with the introduction of the Dominator 85. In this case, 59 of 62 owners questioned were satisfied with their machine. In common with the Dominator 80 the amount of dust was criticised as was the accessibility to the threshing drum and drive belts. Similar findings were arrived at for the Dominator 100, with 85% of owners satisfied with it on the whole. The further development steps incorporated into the Dominator 105 also brought about a clear improvement.

In 1977 the Dominator 85 was sent to the DLG and the Dutch IMAG test centre where it was put through its paces in comparison with the John Deere 975 and Fahr M 1302. In both comparisons the Claas machine obtained a higher performance. However, it became apparent that there were weaknesses when running on slopes. The cleaning losses rose considerably when operating over hillsides. The reason for this was presumably the smaller sieve area.

The Dominator was aimed at large farms and contractors.

The Dominator range was extended both upwards and downwards. This meant low losses could be achieved, even in difficult harvest conditions.

The 3 -D dynamic slope compensation which had made its debut on the CS combine range was now made available on the straw walker combines with the introduction of the Dominator 8 series. The ingenious design adds an uphill swing to the sieve box. This added swing propels short straw and chaff against the force of gravity, maintaining the combine's output across slopes.

The Contour system became an additional feature on the cutter bar. For the first time, this provided automatic ground pressure control. Even more comfort was provided later by the Auto Contour cutter bar which adapted the cutter bar position relative to the ground both in travel direction as well as laterally. Furthermore grain tank volume and the engine strength were being increased constantly. As an example: the Dominator 118 SL Maxi had a grain tank with 7 500 litres capacity and was powered by a big 260 hp diesel engine.

Due to the permanent development efforts which were based on a thoroughly sound design the Dominator family held its own in the marketplace for a remarkably long period of time.

The cab became a standard feature on the 6 series combines.

Up hill and down dale

The full hillside combines were never to gain more than marginal importance due to their high additional cost. The hillside capabilities of the conventional Claas combines over slopes was improved substantially with the 3-D system.

Everyone was used to the fact that stationary threshing machines had to be lined up completely horizontally. Winches were used to raise the individual wheels, then wedges and other devices were placed underneath until the machine was completely level. This precision could never be reached with the combine because the ground surface changes constantly. Therefore different ideas were developed to compensate for the influence of slopes.

The initial attempts are described by Graeme Quick and Wesley Buchele in their book "The Grain Harvesters". The Holt combines from California were equipped with slope compensation as far back as 1892. The first Claas combine MDB was also available in an HT version with slope compensation. The two guide wheels could be cranked up and down to adjust the combine to the field angle.

During the following years the subject of combining over hillsides faded into the background again in Germany. Conventional combines were able to cope reasonably well on slopes of up to 20% anyway. Uphill the crop ran through the combine faster, and downhill it flowed a little slower over the sieves and straw walkers. This had hardly any impact on the overall performance. When there was a sideways slope, the guide plates on the sieves prevented the crop from sliding downhill. If losses on the sieve box went up too much, the driver simply reduced the throughput a little.

The first Claas hillside combine was based on the Dominator 85. The high extra cost meant that it never caught on in Germany.

slope   **with 3-D**   **without 3-D**

effect on the sieve box and there is very little effect as far as the straw walkers are concerned. The crop that is supposed to be cleaned on the sieves slips by gravity to the lower side. The resistance is lower on the uphill side so that the air blast escapes. Then a thick mat of material builds up on the lower side, which is then impossible to aerate. The grain falls out of the back of the machine together with the chaff and the short straw and ends up on the field.

Sperry New Holland were the first company to try and alleviate this problem: their idea was to offer an automatic sieve box levelling control for their big machines. The preparation pan and fans were kept horizontal relative to the ground in addition to the sieve box. At this time Claas was developing the 3-D dynamic slope compensation system. This feature means that the upper sieve is provided with an additional side movement against the slope. The strength and direction of the uphill movement is dependent on the slope position and the slope angle. The crop is kept evenly distributed on the sieve box up to a slope of 20%.

Harvesting across slopes was rendered more difficult as wider cutter bars became available. As cutting widths grew and exceeded 4.5 metres, the front drive wheel on the lower side became subject to extra heavy loadings and then tends to sink into the ground. On the uphill side the cutter bar lifts off from the ground and the cutting height increases. In short stemmed or laid crops cutting losses can occur. With this in mind, Claas subsequently introduced the Auto Contour control to resolve this problem on the wider cutter bars. The cutter bar follows the field's contours not just in travel direction but also laterally. The stubble height is then uniform across the full width.

EIGHT CYLINDER POWER PACK

To increase the performance of the top of the line combines, Claas developed the CS range, replacing the straw walkers with eight separation cylinders.

The conventional straw walker system became the major performance limiting factor on the larger combines. Road transport regulations imposed a limit to the width of threshing and cleaning systems. The axial flow combines imported from America by Case IH at that time were compact machines and it was observed that the forced rotor separation was capable of producing high performance in dry conditions. However, wet and green straw gave no end of trouble to these machines.

Claas decided not to follow this development direction because of the difficult crop conditions in Europe. Instead of this the company created the "Cylinder System" which was introduced on the Dominator 116 CS in 1981. This machine was equipped with a conventional 1.58 metre wide threshing drum. Eight separation cylinders were lined up behind the drum with separation concaves fitted underneath. The threshing concaves had the task of separating as many grains from the straw as possible. The straw was then force-fed to the straw hood by the cylinders. This feed system produced a uniform and fast crop flow. Residual grain was effectively separated from the thin mat of straw. Both the concave spacing and the cylinder rotation speed could be adjusted to match the characteristics of the crop.

The Dominator CS 116 was the first Claas combine without straw walkers.

A THIRD DRUM TAKES THE
STRAIN OFF THE STRAW WALKERS

The accelerator drum brought about a throughput increase of up to 30% in the Mega combine series.

Claas introduced the APS threshing system on the Mega combine range. Unlike the developments by the other manufacturers, an accelerator drum was fitted in front of the main threshing drum.

Increased yields, green straw and other external factors left the threshing drum faced with ever increasing challenges. It became steadily more difficult to achieve the dual aims of separating up to 90% of the grains and then transporting them through the concave.

Some manufacturers engineered a third drum behind the impeller. Just like the threshing drum itself, this additional drum was supposed to get rid of more grain before the crop reached the straw walkers.

Claas decided on a different approach and developed the APS system (Accelerated Pre-Separation). An accelerator drum was added in front of the main threshing drum. This takes the crop from the feed elevator conveyor, accelerates it and transfers it with an increased flow speed to the threshing drum. This means the threshing unit accelerates the crop, which is able to reach very high speeds and the centrifugal forces resulting from this lead to considerably improved threshing performance.

The material is pulled apart additionally by the acceleration process. At any specific output, the grains can pass more easily through the gaps in the concave because the mat of material is that much thinner and more evenly spread across the full width. Additionally there is an extra concave under the accelerator. The grains which are separated by the accelerator are disposed of at an early stage.

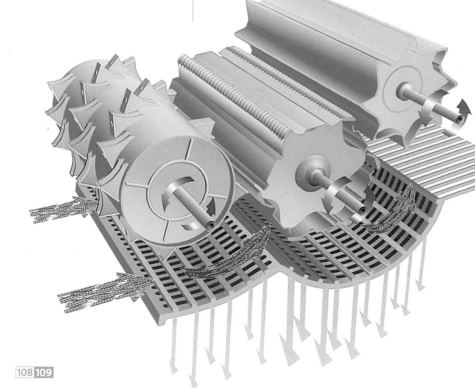

The accelerator drum speeds up the crop flow before passing the material to the drum. The centrifugal forces in the threshing unit are increased and system efficiency improved. Early grain separation is enhanced by the concave under the accelerator.

Unlike other combine brands the accelerator was not added at expense of the straw walker length. Instead the machine was lengthened by 460 mm to the front. The added forward length was possible because the entry angle of the crop to the threshing drum doesn't change if the feeder housing is raised or lowered. The drum has the highest wrap angle available on combines with a right angle threshing drum with 151°.

The APS system first saw the light of day on the Mega 208 and 218 combines. Claas claimed an increased throughput of around 30% versus conventional threshing systems.

Claas promoted the system on the basis of increased performance of up to 30% and pointed out the following advantages:

1. The accelerator takes effect where all grains are still in the crop, in the so-called 100% zone. It isn't located behind the threshing drum where a large part of the grain has already been separated, as is the case with a normal third drum.

2. The crop flow is speeded up and the mat of material becomes thinner and more evenly spread across the channel width. The grains can be separated more easily.

3. The faster crop flow places higher centrifugal forces on the crop, and the separation performance of the threshing drum is improved decisively.

4. The concave underneath the accelerator removes significant quantities of grain before it reaches the threshing drum.

The APS threshing system was introduced in 1993 and installed into the Mega 208 and 218. Both models had a 1.58 metre wide threshing drum and a grain tank with 7 500 litres capacity. They were driven by diesel engines with output rated at 235 or 270 hp. Cutter bars were available between 4.50 and 6.00 metres width. A year afterwards, a family of five straw walker machines followed. These three models were called Mega 202, 203 and 204 and were differentiated from the bigger combines in terms of engine output and grain tank capacity.

Once the APS system had established its reputation in the Mega range, it was installed on the Lexion family.

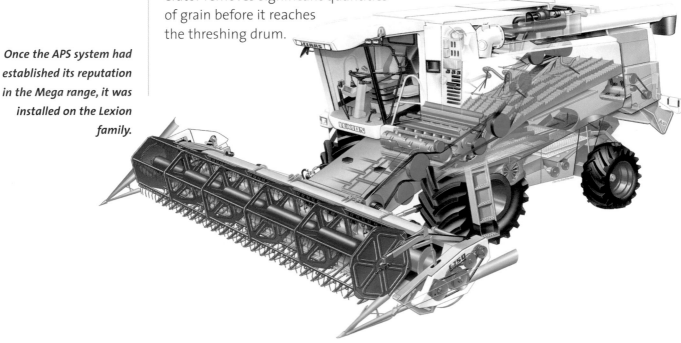

A CLEAN CUT IS VITAL

Claas had quickly realised combines would only catch on in a big way in Europe if the cutter bars, pick-ups and maize headers could cope with the difficult conditions and the combine harvester itself could be used in all different types of crops.

The cutter bar was of vital importance in building a combine for European conditions. Long, damp straw and laid crop conditions didn't make it easy for the combines. Claas took on the challenge of developing what was described as a laid crop cutter bar from the outset. The very first combine — the MDB — was already equipped with crop lifters, for instance. The crop lifters were transferred to the self-propelled combines at a later stage.

The picking up of laid crops was facilitated by the long distance between the knife bar and the intake auger (620 mm). On the other hand, a shorter table width is better suited for working in standing crops because the grain cannot build up

a wall in front of the intake auger. Rotating crop dividers could be added in particularly heavy laid crops.

Further features included the hollow behind the knife bar which captured the loose grain and the coil springs fitted to the hydraulics cylinders. They suspended the cutter bar and improved its contour following characteristics.

The consistency of crop flow through the combine is determined at the cutter bar. This explains why developments in this area have always been subject to close attention at Claas.

At first only the cutter bar and reel height could be adjusted hydraulically. A mechanical adjustment of the reel speed by means of a hand crank then followed. As the combine evolved in terms of sophistication, hydraulic or electrical speed adjustment made it easier to match the machine to different harvest conditions and travel speeds.

With the advent of the Dominator 5 series, a pre-selected cutting height was added to the product offering. The cutter bar returned to its programmed cutting height automatically each time the combine turned round on the headland.

Hydraulic horizontal reel adjustment was added to the range with the 6 series. It made it possible for the driver to quickly modify the position of the reel relative to the cutting edge of the combine. This adjustment comes into its own particularly when harvest conditions within the field are extremely variable (e.g. when there is a frequent transition between laid and standing crops.)

Claas developed the cutter bars for laid crops from the outset. The long distance from the knives to the intake auger is a typical example. Crop lifters were standard from the very beginning.

The Contour cutter bar control then made its debut with the introduction of the 8 combine series. For the first time, the cutter bar could be run with ground contact. This was achieved by linking the automatic cutting height pre-selection with a ground pressure control. The Auto Contour cutter bar introduced later went an important step further by guiding the cutter bar lightly over the surface of the field fully automatically both laterally and in travel direction.

Once the harvest of oil seed rape from the standing crop had established itself in the seventies Claas also turned its attention to rape cutter bars in different cutting widths. The conventional cutting table was extended by 40 to 60 cm. On the right and on the left sides vertical knives were installed, which could be driven either electrically or hydraulically.

Customers who wanted to do without the additional rape cutter bar and the changeover effort involved were catered for when the Vario cutter bar for the Lexion range was introduced in 1998. The Vario cutter bar is extended by 500 mm from the basic position for the rape harvest from the cab. The gaps that open up in the table are covered with special blanking plates. Additional side knives to separate the crop are fitted and a fully functional rape cutter bar is then available.

The cutter bar table is extended by 400 to 600 mm for oil seed rape harvesting. The vertical knives mounted on the sides are either electrically or hydraulically driven.

The Vario cutter bar also had clear advantages in the cereals harvest. The driver could now shorten the cutter bar table from the cab by 100 mm or extend it by 200 mm on the go. This feature made it even easier to adapt the cutter bar to different straw lengths or when crossing isolated areas of laid crop.

The folding cutter bar was another invention aimed at reducing the time needed when moving from one field to another. The first attempt at building

one of these was made by Dechenreiter with the "Adler" or Eagle header. The cutter bar was split in the middle and could be folded upwards. Another supplier, Geringhoff, presented a version in 1989, in which the two halves could be swung on top of one another. Claas introduced a cutter bar of its own two years later. As opposed to Geringhoff design, the Claas cutter bar halves were swung forwards. At first Claas produced a 4.50 metre folding cutter bar which was later added to with a 5.40 metre version.

Pick-ups for swath harvesting

In the first years with the combine, many farms couldn't entirely break with past harvesting traditions. Devices were created for feeding in the crop by hand, to make the transition easier.

Until the seventies oil seed rape was threshed exclusively from the swath. Grass seed, peas and other crops were at first also laid in a swath with a swath mower, where it could mature and dry out. As a result Claas could supply a pick-up drum for the cutter bar, right from the early combine era.

This harvesting method went out of fashion at the end of the seventies. The seed producers had by then developed

rape varieties that ripened more evenly. In addition, the yields were approximately 9% higher in standing crops versus the swath method. This was confirmed by tests carried out by the RKL organisation (Agriculture Rationalisation Committee) which were performed in 1974 on an area of 120 hectares. The higher yield comes as a direct result of reduced losses when the crop is taken on board the combine. In addition, the costs for mowing the swath, which amounted to about 85 DM per hectare, could also be saved.

After some years the pick-up drums were then finally discontinued. At a much later stage, Claas added a pick-up again for export markets, specially for the Eastern European area, which was branded as the rake-up.

Harvesting oil seed rape from the swath featured prominently during the seventies. The crop was mown with a swath mower some two weeks prior to combining. Claas equipped the combines with pick-up drums to gather up the swaths.

Cutting or picking grain maize?

Maize pickers rendered the old cutter headers obsolete quite quickly. Only the cobs and leaves are picked up instead of the complete plant.

Grain maize harvesting was initially done by feeding the whole plant into the combine. The Super pull type combine was available with a single row maize cutter header. When going from grain to maize, the threshing drum and the concave had to be exchanged. There was still a maize cutter header in the product range for the relatively modern Mercator.

These headers were primarily used on smaller areas. The low purchase price was an important feature. The drawback was the large volume of material passing though the combine, which put it under a lot of strain. Throughput suffered considerably and humidity was transferred to the grains. Therefore Claas replaced the maize cutter header with the maize picker as of 1966. The difference is that the combine processes mainly the cobs and leaves. Different types of chopper were fitted under the snapping rollers or behind the picker to fully destroy the plant stems.

There were single row pickers for the small pull type and self-propelled combines. The bigger self-propelled combines could be fitted with two and three row versions. The Senator even could be equipped with a four row header. The range expanded to 8 rows as the years went by. Once more, as four rows or more are harvested, the outer picking units have to be folded for travel on public roads.

Claas introduced a new picker family with conical snapping rolls on the Agritechnica 1999. This special shape initially drags the stems down slowly. Once the cob has been picked, the flow speed increases. This design enables the cobs to be treated more gently.

Special answers for soy, thistles, sunflowers etc.

With its claim of being the harvesting specialist Claas had to offer suitable equipment for all types of special crops. The Claas motto can be summarised as follows: "A Claas combine can harvest everything from primrose seeds to broad beans".

A flexible cutter bar which could run very close to the ground is one example and was designed for the harvest of soy beans. This is because the soy beans grow from the lower part of the stem. These are very close to the ground and often they lie directly on the ground. In addition, soy beans are often cultivated on little furrows in many regions.

Conventional cutter bars can be converted to the harvesting of sunflowers. They are fitted with forward mounted trays to catch the loose seeds that fall

out very early. Claas has developed a special header for the harvest of castor oil together with the French farming organisation Cemagref.

"A Claas combine can harvest everything from primrose seeds to broad beans". A wide range of headers is on offer to back up this motto.

THRESHING CLOSE TO THE ARCTIC CIRCLE

In the far north, where the summer season
is short, combines are still a rarity.

Progress in farming techniques and
hybrid plant development have helped
advance the use of combines into
borderline regions. Claas combines are
now to be found close to the Arctic
Circle. The most northerly Lexion 480
belongs to Unto Touminen, who is a
farmer and contractor in Turku, Finland.
His operation in the west of the country
is situated on the same degree of lati-
tude as Iceland and Alaska.

*The combine fleet of the
Rehnberg brothers is in
operation close to Helsinki.
The two old treasures,
"Europa" and "Huckepack"
still run properly but are no
longer put into the real
harvest.*

The harvesting window is very small in
this country, so he decided to invest in
the flagship combine from Claas.
Gustav and Henrik Rehnberg are
brothers who also both appreciate the
importance of maximum performance
and they too run a Lexion
480 near Helsinki.

In the north of Europe, the growing
conditions are very special. The season
for growing crops is concentrated on
a few summer months of the year.
Farmer Touminen has to always bear

this in mind when planning his own 70 hectares plus the 200 hectares harvested by himself on a contract basis.

In normal years Finland's farmers can start combining in the middle of August, although the harvest then drags on to the beginning of October. The grain harvest is a rather moist affair. The grain has an average humidity ranging from 25 to 35%. The grain on the stalks shimmers more green than gold. In exceptionally warm years like 1999, the grain humidity sinks below the 25% level.

During this exceptional year the Rehnberg brothers could start the harvest in July and were able to put the Lexion

480 back in the barn in the middle of August after a really speedy grain harvest. Within only nine days they had cleared 350 hectares. This corresponds to an hourly work rate of almost five hectares.

The rest of the combine fleet is not quite so fast. The two Dominator 88 combines do about half the acreage of the big Lexion. Then there is another big gap before we get to the Europa and the Huckepack. These vintage machines are well cared for in their old age and are not called upon to do any serious hard work when the brief harvest time comes round in Finland.

High work rates are essential in the brief Finnish summer. The Claas flagship combine has to gather in the moist crop in just a few days.

TWO ROTORS
INSTEAD OF STRAW WALKERS

On the Lexion 480, Claas engineers put conventional threshing together with two axial rotors.

Claas opened up a new performance category with the Lexion 480.

The CS combines demonstrated that the company was on the right track to increasing output with forced separation. The eight cylinder system was too complex so that Claas was forced to look for a simpler system which would be equally effective.

The engineers unveiled their solution in 1995. The conventional threshing system had been married up with a pair of rotors fitted lengthways. The Lexion 480 was the first combine with this hybrid configuration.

The APS threshing system (now 1.7 metres wide) with the accelerator in front of the threshing drum had been taken over from the Mega. For this bigger machine the threshing drum diameter was increased to 600 mm. This enables the separation area in the main threshing system to be increased significantly. The straw impeller was

The APS system on the Lexion 480 came equipped with a larger threshing drum. A pair of rotors replaced the straw walkers.

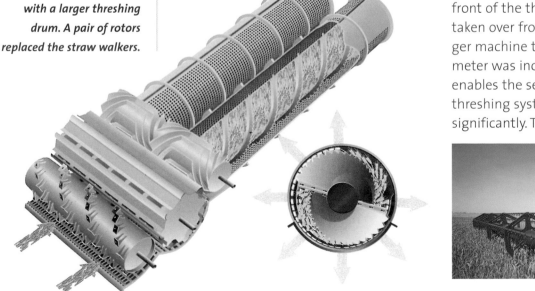

given an additional task: it divides the crop into two streams and guides it onto the axial rotors. The spiral flights on the rotors feed the straw actively to the back of the combine, permanently mixing it as it proceeds. A high crop speed is reached generating increased centrifugal forces which guarantee an extremely effective forced separation of the last grains still captured in the straw. The machine can be matched to variations in crop characteristics either by adjusting the threshing drum speed and concave spacing as well as by modifying the rotor speed.

The Lexion 480 marked not only the dawn of a new system for secondary separation. Claas also introduced a whole range of other performance enhancing features. The Lexion was designed with a completely new Vista cab. The built-in on-board Cebis (Claas Electronic On-Board Information System) computer takes over a whole number of tasks for the driver. Besides the monitoring of the vital machine

functions the driver can carry out the setting up of the combine electronically as well. Yield mapping as a prerequisite for precision farming is also built into the Cebis programme.

Improved throughput was only one part of the story. Enhanced operator comfort and control were of equal importance.

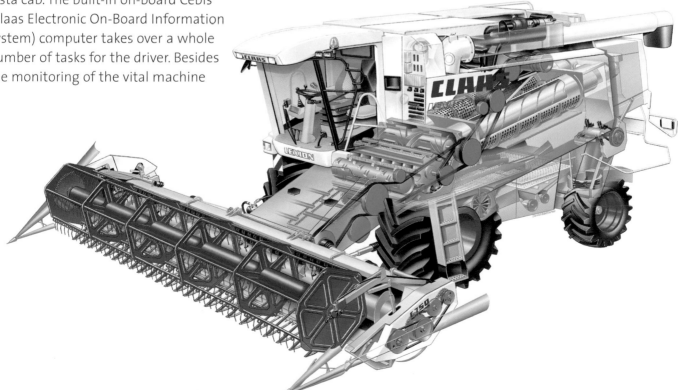

The Lexion 480 is driven by a 400 hp diesel engine. The grain tank has a capacity of 10 500 litres. Cutter bars with widths of up to 9.00 metres are available. Another innovation was the quick hydraulic and electrical connection between the combine and the header with one single plug.

A completely new straw chopper does justice to the increased requirements for even distribution of chopped straw and chaff with cutting widths up to 9.00 m. A pair of spreading fans are situated below the straw chopper and these blow the straw and chaff over the full nine metre width with a characteristic tail wagging action. The range can be set from the cab to correct for side winds.

In 1996 the Lexion range was added to with the straw walker machines. All of the main features of the big Lexion were incorporated into this model range, with the exception of the rotor separation.

The 450 mm threshing drum steps aside

Claas had adapted a 450 mm threshing drum diameter right from the very start of their combine designs. A smaller drum diameter was less expensive and took up less space inside the combine. In addition, it required less power than a big drum to get it turning at its right speed. In maintenance terms, a smaller drum was easier to balance than a big one.

For many years, there was no need to rethink the philosophy. Performance could be increased by widening the threshing channel, and the critical road travel width had not yet been reached. In the earlier days of combining, harvesting damp crops was also of little significance. These parameters began to change when large combines appeared in the early seventies.

The competition turned to larger drum diameters as a means of increasing performance: Fahr 460 to 600 mm, IHC 460 to 560 mm, John Deere at 610 mm MF at 560 mm and New Holland Clayson at 600 mm. These producers claimed that a large diameter threshing drum grabbed the crop more vigorously and reduced the risk of wrapping in comparison with Claas. They further propagated the idea that a larger radius keeps the speed of rotation more constant in changing harvest conditions.

The large concave wrap angle does mean that threshing is more thorough, at least in theory. This could not be confirmed, although the DLG testing centre tried it out in 1976. The threshing losses on the Dominator 85 were no higher than on the John Deere 975 with 610 mm and the Fahr 1300 with a 600 mm drum.

The larger wrap angle of the bigger drum enables more grain per metre drum width to be separated and this takes some of the work off the straw walkers. This effect was utilised with the Mega range with the addition of an accelerator drum in front of the main threshing drum. This enabled separation efficiency to be increased despite retaining the existing main drum size.

The 450 mm was a characteristic of Claas combines for close on 60 years. It was only abandoned when the Lexion 480 was introduced with 600 mm diameter.

With the Lexion 480, Claas finally made a departure from the 450 mm drum diameter. A 600 mm drum was engineered in order to increase the primary separation area. After almost 60 years, Claas had finally said goodbye to the typical, characteristic 450 mm drum size which had always been such a popular source of debate.

This book depicts in detail the combine harvester story as revealed by Claas. Coincidentally the family company from Westfalia celebrated a special anniversary at the start of the 2002 selling season. It marked 66 years of Claas combines.

THE STORY IS FAR FROM OVER

This was the occasion for the company to present the whole story beginning with the MDB right up to today in a live presentation and demonstration.

The demonstration of the MDB and the Lexion 480 on the same field made perfectly clear to everyone who attended just how enormous the steps made in harvesting technology really are.

Nobody can predict what the grain harvest will look like 66 years from now. There are plenty of new developments in the pipeline, aimed at even more efficient harvesting with reduced losses and still less manual labour involved. It remains to be seen whether another farming revolution takes place. Whatever happens, the story of the combine harvester will certainly go on for ever.

Claas company chronology

1887 Franz Claas senior sets up a company in Clarholz for the production of centrifuges.

1894 The company increased to 6 employees and was already working with steam power.

1900 Franz Claas designed a first straw binder which he patented as a device for reapers and for cutting grain.

1900 A farm contracting business is established as a second key activity of Claas. It employed 20 to 30 persons at its peak.

1913 August Claas takes over the straw binder production from his father. He writes to the Herzebrock town hall: *"I hereby inform you most obediently that I have been running my own business since April 8th, 1913. I employ 2 fitters, 1 manual worker and produce straw binders".*

1914 August, Bernhard and Franz Claas set up the company "Gebrüder Claas" (Claas Brothers) on January 12th, 1914. The Herzebrock administration received the notification from Franz Claas Senior that the Claas company had adopted a new name:
"I inform you politely that the company is now continued under the name of "Claas Brothers". We will carry out the production of the straw binders at the address of Heerde 4. We register ourselves with this business: August, Bernhard, Franz Claas Junior".

1915 The Franz Claas company suffers from financial difficulties. In addition the Claas brothers are called up for military service in the First World War. Franz Claas Senior shut the companies down in Clarholz and moved to Harsewinkel.

1919 The Claas brothers buy the site of a brickworks in Harsewinkel. They start with the production of agricultural machinery (straw binders) in the factory buildings. As the business expanded, the old buildings were later pulled down.

The infrastructure was poor. Harsewinkel was connected to the town of Warendorf only by a railway and a secondary road. The production conditions were also very rudimentary. Only a few machines were on hand that needed power, and this was provided by a locomobile which was previously used for threshing. It had been in the family's possession for quite a while and was overhauled for use in the plant.

The Claas brothers purchased the brick works in Harsewinkel in 1919. The first buildings for manufacturing farm equipment are visible in the background.

1921 AND 1922 The company capacity was not fully utilised with farm equipment. Chair making and woodwork fill the gap.

MAY 18TH, 1921 August Claas registers the knotter with a special lip to the German patent office. This turned out to be the decisive breakthrough. Its reliability forced the imported straw binders that dominated the German market out of the market.

Claas is the first business in Harsewinkel to develop from artisanal to industrial status. The company later became the town's largest employer and it begins to play a decisive role in the commercial development of the complete region.

1923 Claas takes part in the annual exhibition of the German agricultural association (DLG) for the first time and is awarded the DLG silver commemorative coin for their straw binder in 1924.

1920 TO 1929 The demand for agricultural machinery rises rapidly. This was caused by a strong wave of mechanisation in farming. The first exports were handled in this time. The markets included Holland, France and later England. The number of employees at Claas multiplies from 20 to approximately 275 people. The factory area increases from 387 m^2 to 6 100 m^2.

1922 Development of the first Claas fertiliser spreaders, which went into production in the year of 1924.

1928 The first straw baler for fitting to stationary threshing machines is produced.

1929 The world economic crisis takes its toll on demand for farming equipment which diminishes severely. By 1932 more than 34% of the Claas employees have lost their jobs.

1930 August Claas starts discussions with Professor Karl Vormfelde, with whom he is acquainted, and they discuss the feasibility of the development of a combine for European harvest conditions. Walter Brenner, an assistant of Vormfelde, joins the company.

1936 Market introduction of the first pick-up baler.

Claas manufactured straw balers to fit to stationary threshing machines.

The first pick-up baler made by the Claas brothers.

1937 The first combine harvester is added to the Claas product range. The new machine, which is christened MDB and has a lateral crop flow, then went into series production. The hundredth machine was delivered to a customer just two years later.

The MDB was the result of seven years of intensive research.

The number of employees in the business rose from 253 to 520 between 1933 and 1939 as a direct result of the company's positive development. Many of the employees still had their own small scale farming activities at home. For them, the farming business became a sideline whilst the job at Claas took on more and more importance as the business grew.

The working week was 56 hours long. From Monday to Friday the working day was 10 hours and on Saturdays six hours. The shifts began 6.30 in the morning and finished at 6.30 pm. There was a 90 minute lunch break.

1943 The company's production facilities have to be switched over to supplying the war effort. Up till then the company had produced 1 400 combines in Harsewinkel. Preparations had been made for production of armaments at the start of the war. The machine tools had to be set up so they could produce ammunition casings when required. The management nevertheless managed to maintain the production of agricultural machinery right up to 1943. This was only made possible by the fact that the production of agricultural machinery had been classified as essential to the war effort.

The Claas company was hit hard by the loss of the labour force, which was called up for military service on a steady basis. At first many women were employed to fill their places. Then prisoners of war were employed and they came from France, Yugoslavia and the Soviet Union. 336 prisoners of war were employed by Claas in the year 1944.

Whilst the war was still going on, the people at Claas had started designing a completely new combine harvester. This was the inception of the Super combine.

1945 Work in the factory is resumed immediately after hostilities ceased in May. The buildings had fortunately escaped from war damage. The British military government had, however, confiscated parts of the factory premises. In addition, many qualified employees had not returned alive or were still in captivity and no replacements could be found for them.

1946 In the course of the year a workers' committee is elected at Claas for the first time. It had the responsibility for a different range of tasks than today's workers' committees, though. The management hoped on the one hand that it could provide support against possible dismantling of the plant for reparation purposes and on the other hand the idea was to involve the staff in decision making. In addition, the workers' committee dealt with obtaining food, fuel and spare parts for bicycles. The bicycle was the only available means of transportation for the employees at that time. In addition, the employee representation fought very strongly for the workers who carried out farming in their spare time.

1946 With 100 employees the production of the straw binders, pick-up balers and the Super combine recommences. The production of seed drills starts at the same time.

1947 The covered factory area increases to 45 000 m². Construction of the main assembly building is begun.

1948 Claas builds a foundry in the Gütersloh district of Blankenhagen.

1949 The number of employees climbs to 500. By the following year 600 people are employed by Claas.

1950 Claas takes part in farm equipment exhibitions in Paris and Brussels.

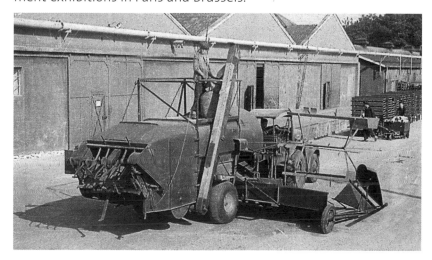

1951 The 5 000th combine is produced at Claas. The production has been increasing every year and soon reaches 800 units. Even at this stage, the company places great value on efficient production and invests heavily in modern manufacturing methods.

1951 178 German refugees and exiles are now working at Claas. This corresponds to 23.3% of the labour force, so the company sponsors housing programmes for them.

1953 Claas introduces the first self-propelled combine, the "Hercules". The name had to be changed to SF later on.

The legendary "Super" combine was produced in Harsewinkel from 1946 onwards. Its success is underlined by the fact that some 65 000 machines were produced.

1954 The production volume is increased to over 13 000 combines per annum.

1954 AND 1956 Claas exhibits at the Leipzig fair in communist East Germany.

1955 Claas specialises on the production of combines and pick-up balers. The current headquarters building in front of the plant is completed. The commercial and engineering functions can then be housed together. This makes it possible to achieve a tighter organisation and greater efficiency. Up to this point the erection of production plants had priority. The Claas brothers had always made a point of avoiding a big bureaucracy.

The main plant in Harsewinkel grows and grows.

1956 The factory in Metz is founded for the production of balers. This investment is also aimed at better serving the important French market. Metz was chosen because of the good rail and road connections plus the availability of adequate qualified employees.

1958 The covered production area has increased to 75 000 m².

1960 Over 16 000 combines are now being sold by the company every year.

1960 Opening of a new production facility in Schloss Holte, a town in between Harsewinkel and Paderborn. Hydraulic parts are to be produced there.

1956 Claas establishes another plant in Paderborn. Transmissions and axles are to be manufactured in this facility. The hydraulics production is integrated into this facility later. Company busses had been used to transport workers from the Paderborn region to Harsewinkel plant till now. With the factory set up directly in Paderborn, Claas brings the work to where the workers are.

1961 The production of pick-up balers is started in Metz.

1962 There are extreme labour shortages in the region. As a result, 130 Spanish guest workers were recruited for the Harsewinkel factory.

1962 The 100 000th combine rolls off the line. It is a "Matador". The factory site now covers 50 000 m², of which some 11 500 m² are under roof.

1964 The economic upturn leads to an increase in the number of employees to 3 300.

1965 The daily production is increased to 120 machines with work being done in 9.5 hours shifts.

1966 The factory premises get their own rail link. Before this came on line, several hundred combines had to be driven through the town to the station every day. Every day, the shipments are loaded onto 80 rail flatbeds in two shift working.

1966 Claas supplies 60 Matador Gigant combines to Canada.

1969 Claas takes over the Bautz company, a manufacturer of harvesting machines in the Saulgau in the upper Swabian area in the south of Germany. After the takeover, machines for the forage harvest are manufactured there.

1970 The total labour force in all the Claas plants reaches a total of 7 996.

1970 Completion of the range with the takeover of the Speiser forage harvest chain. Shift of production from Göppingen to Saulgau.

1971 A new product line aimed at tropical and subtropical areas is developed. The sugar cane harvester is christened "Libertadora".

For the first time in its history the company turns in a multi-million loss in the 1970/71 business year. Only 6 700 combines and 6 600 pick-up balers are sold in this tough year. This is due to a recession in the agricultural machinery business. Claas is hit hard by this development, because only 10% of the company's sales volume are achieved outside of farming. In addition, fluctuations on the foreign exchange markets lead to a strong price increase of the products sold to export markets. Claas is particularly vulnerable to such currency shifts with an export share of approx 75%.

1972 The company tries to open up new markets and establish itself outside Europe. The Ford Tractor Division

August Claas, Doctor of Engineering, hands over the 200 000th combine to John Steven from Haddington, Scotland on the 16th of August 1968.

Bautz was taken over by Claas in 1969. The factory in Saulgau is focussed on forage harvesting equipment.

in Michigan assumes responsibility for the marketing of Claas combines in the USA. The planned sales figures are, however, not achieved in the years to come.

1972 Claas makes an application to the North-Rhine Westphalia state government for a guarantee for its long-term loans amounting to 40 million DM. This is to be accompanied by a restructuring programme and widening of the production range to secure the guarantee. In connection with this situation, the supervisory board is replaced and the number of partners cut drastically. After five years the loan guarantee is no longer needed and can then be revoked.

The Super pull type combine was built in Harsewinkel until 1978. The share of self-propelled combines grew steadily over the years.

1973 The production can be increased to 8 500 combines in the 1972/73 financial year. The first Claas self-propelled forage harvester is introduced.

1976 The first Claas round baler, the Rollant 85, makes its market debut.

1977 For the first time in its history Claas has to go onto short working weeks. The reasons are to be found in structural and economic difficulties. The short time working is introduced to avoid the need for dismissals.

1978 Transformation of the company into Claas OHG (unlimited liability trading company).

1980 The production has to be interrupted once more for some days every month, due to a background of falling worldwide harvesting machinery sales.

1980 Claas opens a sales company of its own in Great Britain.

1981 Claas sells the 1 000th combine to its biggest individual customer, the Hungarian I.K.R. This is an association of 235 large state-run farms. Claas now ranks 407 in the list of the 500 largest German businesses.

1982 Work is discontinued for six days before Christmas. The investment climate in farming is once again unfavourable. The three foundries in Bielefeld, Gütersloh and Saulgau are combined within a single company entity, Claas Guss, based in Bielefeld.

1983 The Jaguar 675 to 695 self-propelled forage harvester family is introduced.

1984 For the first time in the company's history, the sales volume exceeds the one billion DM level in the 1983/84 financial year. The employees can now purchase their own shares in the company. To this end an employee participation company, the CMG, is founded.

1986 About 75% of the staff are affected by short time as a result of the poor economic environment.

1990 About 2 000 employees are affected by short time for a week.

1991 Claas Manufacturing Technology Division (CFT) moves to a factory of its own in Beelen, close to Harsewinkel.

1992 The Technoparc visitor centre is opened in front of the Harsewinkel plant.

1993 The Ranger telescopic handler is added to the Claas product range by means of a joint venture with Sanderson Teleporters Ltd. in Great Britain. The

The Technoparc in Harsewinkel is the exhibition and information centre of the company.

1987 Short time working at Claas in January and February. In the course of the year the labour force has to be reduced by 900 people.

1988 Claas introduces the Quadrant large bale baler to the market.

1988 The company returns to the black after one year with a loss. The 1987/88 financial year balance sheet shows a profit again.

Mega combine range with the APS threshing system makes its debut.

1994 Claas starts with the development of agricultural software for yield mapping, precision farming and farm management.

1995 Claas OHG and Claas Maschinenfabrik GmbH are joined together and form the new company entity called Claas KGaA (share owning partnership).

1995 Dr. Helmut Claas retires from the active management of the company and becomes the chairman of the supervisory board and the partners' committee.

1996 The Lexion combine family is introduced.

A joint venture is entered into, in which Caterpillar markets Lexion combines in North America.

1997 Joint venture with Caterpillar. Caterpillar plans to sell yellow Lexion combines under their brand name in North America and Claas is to market the Challenger belt drive tractor from Caterpillar in Europe.

Claas takes over a factory in Törökszentmiklos (Hungary) for the production of components.

1998 Claas forms an independent company called Agrocom GmbH & Co agricultural systems KG by the takeover of software designers Klöpper & Wiege and sets up for business in Bielefeld.

1999 Formation of Claas Financial Services for the financing, leasing and renting of Claas products.

The Claas Foundation is established. Its aim is the furtherance of education in areas of science and research, principally in the areas of farm equipment and adjacent fields.

2000 A new logistics centre for Claas spare parts starts operating in Hamm-Uentrop. A new Claas sales company is established in Argentina.

A new Jaguar forage harvester range is introduced to the market. The Medion combine range replaces most of the Dominator series. The Claas Foundation awards grants to students of the field of agricultural technology for the first time. Helmut Claas, chairman of the company's supervisory board, is awarded an honorary doctorship from the university of Stuttgart-Hohenheim for his contribution to the development of modern farm equipment.

MODEL LIST

	First year of production	Cutter bar width m	Drum width mm	Engine hp
Mäh-Dresch-Binder	1936	2.10		Pull type
Super	1946	2.10	1 250	Pull type
Hercules - SF	1953	2.40	1 250	56
Junior	1953	1.50	1 250	Pull type
Super 500	1955	2.10	1 250	Pull type
Huckepack	1956	2.10	800	12 + 23
Europa	1958	2.10	800	42
Columbus	1958	1.80	800	27
Super Automatic	1958	2.10	1 250	Pull type
Junior Automatic	1959	1.80	1 250	Pull type
Matador Gigant	1961	3.00	1 250	87
Matador Standard	1962	2.60	1 250	56
Mercur	1963	2.60	1 060	52
Senator	1966	4.20	1 250	105
Mercator	1967	3.60	1 250	95
Garant	1967	2.40	1 060	Pull type
Comet	1967	1.80	800	29
Cosmos	1967	2.10	800	38
Consul	1967	2.60	1 060	68
Protector	1968	2.60	1 250	68
Corsar	1969	2.40	800	52
Dominator 80	1970	4.50	1 320	120
Compact 20	1970	1.72	580	24
Compact 25	1970	2.10	960	34
Dominator 100	1971	5.10	1 580	170
Mercator 70	1972	3.60	1 250	105
Mercator 60	1972	3.00	1 250	95
Mercator 50	1972	2.60	1 250	72
Dominator 105	1974	4.50	1 580	175
Dominator 85	1974	3.90	1 320	120
Compact 30	1975	2.40	960	50
Mercator 75	1975	3.60	1 250	105
Dominator 106	1978	4.50	1 580	205
Dominator 96	1978	4.50	1 320	150
Dominator 76	1978	3.60	1 060	120
Dominator 56	1978	2.70	1 060	85
Dominator 85 H[2]	1979	4.50	1 320	150
Dominator 66	1979	3.00	1 060	102

[2] with side hill compensation

First year of production is the year the product appeared in the price list.

Pre-series machines were sometimes sold earlier.

The German price list is valid from October to September.

Full availability was often a year later. For this reason there may be some discrepancies between first year of production and appearance in the price list.

Cutter bar, grain tank volume and engine power always refer to the smallest option.

The policy of continuous improvement means that these figures were often revised over the years.

No. of straw walkers	Grain tank volume l
One piece	Bagging platform
One piece	Bagging platform[1]
4	Bagging platform[1]
One piece	Bagging platform[1]
One piece	Bagging platform[1]
3	Bagging platform[1]
3	Bagging platform[1]
3	Bagging platform[1]
One piece	1 700
One piece	1 100
4	2 155
4	
4	1 700
4	3 200
4	2 700
4	1 800
3	1 350
3	1 700
4	2 000
4	2 000
3	1 700
5	3 400
3	850
5	1 100
6	5 500
4	3 000
4	2 500
4	2 000
6	5 500
5	4 000
5	1 900
4	3 000
6	6 500
5	5 200
4	4 200
4	2 500
5	3 000
4	2 500

[1] became available later with an optional grain tank

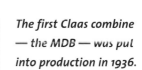

The first Claas combine — the MDB — was put into production in 1936.

65 000 Super combines were built, turning it into a legendary name.

The Compact was designed for smaller sized farms.

The first Senator was presented in 1966 and was later superseded by the Mercator family.

MODEL LIST

	First year of production	Cutter bar width m	Drum width mm	Engine hp
Dominator 86	1980	3.90	1 320	120
Dominator 116 CS[3]	1981	5.70	1 580	250
Dominator 48	1981	2.70	1 060	75
Dominator 38	1981	2.40	800	65
Dominator 68	1982	3.00	1 060	100
Dominator 58	1982	3.00	1 060	85
Dominator 115 CS[3]	1984	5.10	1 320	250
Dominator 114 CS[3]	1984	5.10	1 320	221
Dominator 112 CS[3]	1984	4.50	1 320	170
Dominator 108	1985	4.50	1 580	221
DOMINATOR 98	1985	4.50	1 320	150
Dominator 88	1985	3.90	1 320	120
Dominator 78	1985	3.60	1 060	120
Dominator 98 Maxi	1988	4.50	1 320	200
Dominator 108 Maxi	1989	4.50	1 580	221
Dominator 118 Maxi	1990	4.50	1 580	260
Commandor 228 CS	1990	6.00	1 580	330
Mega 218	1993	6.00	1 580	270
Mega 208	1993	5.10	1 580	235
Mega 204	1994	4.50	1 320	200
Mega 203	1994	4.50	1 320	170
Mega 202	1994	3.90	1 320	160
Lexion 480	1996	7.50	1 700	340
Lexion 460	1997	7.50	1 700	300
Lexion 450	1997	6.60	1 700	275
Lexion 440	1997	6.00	1 700	250
Lexion 430	1997	5.40	1 420	240
Lexion 420	1997	5.40	1 420	220
Lexion 410	1997	4.50	1 420	190
Lexion 405	1997	4.50	1 420	170
Medion 340	2000	5.10	1 580	180
Medion 320	2000	3.90	1 320	147
Medion 310	2000	3.60	1 320	136
Lexion 470	2001	6.00	1 420	320
Lexion 460 Evolution	2001	6.00	1 700	320
Lexion 430 Evolution	2001	4.50	1 420	260
Medion 330	2001	3.90	1 320	220

First year of production is the year the product appeared in the price list.

Pre-series machines were sometimes sold earlier.

The German price list is valid from October to September.

Full availability was often a year later. For this reason there may be some discrepancies between first year of production and appearance in the price list.

Cutter bar. grain tank volume and engine power always refer to the smallest option.

The policy of continuous improvement means that these figures were often revised over the years.

[3] these products were later branded as Commandor combines

No. of straw walkers	Grain tank volume l
5	4 600
Cylinder system	8 000
4	2 400
3	2 100
4	3 200
4	2 700
Cylinder system	7 000
Cylinder system	7 000
Cylinder system	6 000
6	6 500
5	5 200
5	4 600
4	4 200
5	6 200
6	7 500
6	7 500
Cylinder system	10 000
6	7 500
6	7 500
5	6 200
5	6 200
5	5 200
ROTO PLUS	10 500
6	9 600
6	8 600
6	8 100
5	7 800
5	7 300
5	6 300
5	5 500
6	8 200
5	6 500
5	5 800
ROTO PLUS	9 600
6	9 600
5	7 800
5	7 200

The Commandor had cylinder separation in place of straw walkers.

The Mega with the APS threshing system was unveiled in 1993.

Claas developed the Crop Tiger for rice harvesting in Asia.

The Lexion family appeared in the field in 1996.

MODEL INDEX

Combine model	Page	Combine model	Page
Columbus	59 ff., 138	Dominator 86	112, 139
Comet	72 ff., 138	Dominator 88	95, 119, 139
Commandor 228 CS	103, 139	Dominator 96	94, 112, 138
Compact 20	82 ff., 138	Dominator 98	95, 139
Compact 25	82 ff., 138	Dominator 100	90 ff., 138
Compact 30	82 ff., 138	Dominator 105	93, 112., 138
Consul	72 ff., 138	Dominator 106	94, 102, 112, 138
Corsar	72 ff., 138	Dominator 108	95, 139
Cosmos	72 ff., 138	Dominator 116 CS	101 ff., 139
		Dominator 118 Maxi	96, 139
Dominator 38	95, 139	Dominator 198 VX-AL	99
Dominator 48	95, 139		
Dominator 56	94, 112, 138	Europa	59 ff., 85, 119, 138
Dominator 66	112, 138		
Dominator 76	94, 112, 138	Garant	49, 138
Dominator 78	95, 139		
Dominator 78 SL-AL	99	Hercules - SF	52 ff., 58, 76, 129, 138
Dominator 80	77, 90 ff., 138	Huckepack	56 ff., 119, 138
Dominator 85	93, 98, 112, 123, 138	Junior	46, 49, 85, 138
Dominator 85 H	94, 97 ff., 138	Junior Automatic	47, 49, 138